Smoking, drinking and drug use among young people in England in 2000

Smoking, drinking and drug use among young people in England in 2000

Edited by
Richard Boreham and Andrew Shaw

Principal Authors
Harriet Becher, Richard Boreham, Peter Emery, Kerstin Hinds,
Jim Jamison, Ian Schagen.

LONDON: THE STATIONERY OFFICE

The full text of this publication has been made available to you on the Internet.
You can find this at:
http://www.official-documents.co.uk/documents/doh/sddyp/survey.htm.

http://www.doh.gov.uk/public/sddsurvey.htm.

Published with the permission of the Department of Health on behalf of the
Controller of Her Majesty's Stationery Office.

ISBN 0113225628

Designed by Davenport Associates.
Printed in the United Kingdom for The Stationery Office.
NP75778   C8 11/01

Contents

Acknowledgements

Social surveys are always the work of a team. The editors take full responsibility for the content of this report, but gratefully acknowledge the contribution of those colleagues who carried out the fieldwork and assisted with the editing and other stages of the survey.

The authors thank schools for their co-operation and, most important of all, the pupils who took part in the survey.

Notes to tables

1. Percentages do not add to 100% because of rounding.

2. A few children failed to answer each question. These 'no answers' have been excluded from the analysis, and so tables that describe the same population may have slightly varying bases.

3. Percentages based on fewer than 50 cases are shown in square brackets because of the relatively large sampling errors attached to small numbers.

4. Percentages based on fewer than 30 cases are not shown.

5. The following convention has been used

   0 = less than 0.5%, but not zero

   - = Zero

6. In tables where age is a variable, those aged 16 have been included with the 15 year olds. This is because the survey did not include pupils in year 12, and the small number of 16 year olds sampled from year 11 are not representative of all schoolchildren aged 16. Similarly pupils aged 10 have been included with 11 year olds.

7. The school year classification is based on the years or forms of maintained secondary schools. The school years of pupils attending middle and upper schools and some non-maintained schools have been adjusted accordingly.

Summary of main findings

The main purpose of this survey was to continue to monitor smoking, drinking and drug use among secondary school children aged 11-15. Information was obtained from more than 7,000 pupils in 225 schools throughout England during the autumn term of 2000.

Smoking prevalence and cigarette consumption (Chapter 3)

In 2000, 10% of pupils aged 11-15 were regular cigarette smokers (defined as usually smoking at least one cigarette a week). This proportion had decreased from 13% in 1996 to 9% in 1999. The marginal increase in 2000 (from 9% to 10%) was not sufficient to mark a clear reversal of this trend, though it does suggest a steadier fall since 1996 than did the 1999 figure.

Prevalence of smoking was strongly related to age. Only 1% of 11 year olds were regular smokers compared with 23% of 15 year olds.

In the early 1980s, boys and girls were equally likely to smoke. Since then girls have been consistently more likely to smoke than boys. In 2000, 12% of girls were regular smokers, compared with 9% of boys. This gender difference was not present among 11 and 12 year olds, but first appeared at age 13, and was maintained at 14 and 15.

Although girls were more likely to smoke, boys who were regular smokers had smoked more cigarettes in the last week than girls who were regular smokers (an average of 50 compared with 44 for girls). The number of cigarettes smoked by regular smokers has remained quite stable over the entire period since 1982.

Dependence on smoking and family attitudes towards smoking (Chapter 4)

Pupils' own assessment of their dependence on smoking was related to the length of time that they had smoked. Pupils who had been regular smokers for more than a year were markedly more likely to indicate that they were dependent on cigarettes. For example, 72% of these pupils said that they would find it difficult not to smoke for a week and 83% that they would find it difficult to give up smoking altogether. The respective figures for those who had smoked regularly for less than one year were 39% and 58%.

Although largely agreed on the difficulty of giving up smoking, longer-term smokers were quite evenly split about whether or not they wished to do so. Forty two per cent of those who had been regular smokers for more than a year indicated that they would like to give up altogether. Fewer (34%) of those who had been regular smokers for less time said that they wished to give up.

The great majority of pupils perceived that their families had negative attitudes towards smoking; 88% of pupils said that their parents would either stop them smoking or try to persuade them not to smoke. Perceived family attitudes were related to smoking status. Pupils who did not smoke generally felt that if they started smoking, their parents would stop them (65%) rather than try to persuade them to give up (25%). In contrast, regular smokers were less likely to say that their parents would stop them from smoking (21%), and more likely to say their parents would try to persuade them to give up (54%).

Previous research had suggested that parental attitudes were also related to children's age. That is, parents would be more likely to stop younger children smoking, whereas parents of older children would prefer the less firm option of persuading them not to smoke. However, an analysis of family attitudes by age and smoking status together showed that in this survey differences in parental attitudes were primarily explained by smoking status and that age made little difference. It is not clear, though, whether perceived parental attitudes affected smoking behaviour or, conversely, whether attitudes were sometimes adjusted when smoking became a reality.

Where children get cigarettes (Chapter 5)

A large majority of regular smokers usually bought cigarettes from shops, with 80% mentioning this source in 2000. This percentage was consistently even higher (85%- 89%) from 1982 to 1998, but it is not yet possible to be sure that purchasing of cigarettes by pupils from shops is on a downward trend. Since 1982, the proportions of regular smokers obtaining cigarettes from other sources have increased markedly. In 2000, 22% of regular smokers mentioned vending machines as a source of cigarettes, 37% bought cigarettes from other people, and 50% were given cigarettes by friends. The questionnaire addresses sources of cigarettes rather than volume, so these results indicate that pupils are using a wider range of sources to obtain cigarettes without implying an increase in cigarette consumption.

Although the proportion of regular smokers buying cigarettes from shops declined only after 1998, there is evidence of a longer term decline in purchasing from shops among all pupils. The proportion of all pupils who had tried to buy cigarettes from a shop in the last year fell from 27% in 1986 (when the question was introduced) to 19% in 2000. There was also an increase in the proportion of this group who had been refused the purchase of cigarettes on at least one occasion in the last year (45% in 2000, up from 31% in 1986).

The average number of cigarettes bought by pupils at their last purchase has been decreasing. Among those who bought cigarettes, the proportions buying packs of twenty cigarettes fell from 54% in 1988 to 32% in 2000, with a corresponding rise in purchasing of packs of ten cigarettes from 38% to 60%. However, there has been no decline over this period in the total number of cigarettes smoked by current smokers.

Drinking in the previous week (Chapter 7)

Twenty four per cent of pupils had had an alcoholic drink in the previous week. This proportion has fluctuated between 20% and 27% since the question was introduced in 1988, but with no sustained increase or decrease over time.

As with cigarette smoking, drinking was strongly related to age. Only 5% of 11 year olds had drunk alcohol in the last week compared with 49% of 15 year olds.

In most previous surveys boys had been more likely than girls to have drunk in the last week. In 2000, there was no significant difference overall in the proportions of boys (25%) and girls (23%) who drank, although a few more 15 year old boys than girls had had a drink in the last week (51% compared with 45%).

Over the past decade, two types of drink have gained substantial popularity among young drinkers. The proportion having drunk spirits within the previous week has increased from 35% in 1990 to 59% in 2000. Alcopops, introduced onto the market in 1995, were drunk by 62% of drinkers in 2000. The introduction of alcopops has broadened the range of drinks consumed by drinkers, but does not seem to have affected the overall proportion of pupils who drink. In 2000, fewer pupils (20%) had drunk shandy than had their counterparts in 1990 (31%). The proportions drinking other types of drinks, including beer/lager/cider (75% in 2000) and wine (44%), have remained fairly stable.

Although the proportion of pupils who drank in the previous week has fluctuated rather than increased over time, there has been a clear increase in the amount of alcohol consumed by those who drank. Estimated average consumption in the previous week rose from 5.3 units in 1990 to 10.4 units in 2000. The increase in consumption was concentrated on spirits, beer (along with lager and cider) and alcopops (which were first asked about in 1996). The amount of other types of drink consumed remained fairly constant.

The increase in alcohol consumed in the previous week by drinkers was seen among both boys (5.7 units in 1990, 11.6 in 2000) and girls (4.7 units in 1990, 9.1 in 2000). Beer, lager, cider and shandy account for approximately half the amount drunk by boys, and a third of the amount drunk by girls, among whom alcopops accounted for a quarter, spirits a fifth and wine (or fortified wine) a further fifth of the alcohol drunk.

Usual drinking behaviour (Chapter 8)

Forty percent of pupils had never had a whole alcoholic drink, although this figure was much higher among 11 year olds (76%) than 15 year olds (14%). By the age of 14, a large majority of pupils have had an alcoholic drink.

The proportion of pupils who usually drink at least once a week has fluctuated between 16% and 20% since the question was first asked in 1996, but with no consistent increase or decrease over time.

Just under half (46%) of pupils who currently drink never buy alcohol, a figure which has remained at around this level since the question was first asked in 1996. Purchasing from off-licences (17% in 2000) or shops/supermarkets (9%) has become markedly less common over this period, whereas increasing numbers have been purchasing from friends or relatives (17% in 2000).

Drug use (Chapter 10)

Pupils had high levels of awareness of illegal drugs. In 2000, the proportions who had heard of cannabis (88%), cocaine (86%) and heroin (85%) approached nearly nine in ten. Even among 11 year olds, as many as three quarters had heard of each of these drugs, though awareness of other drugs such as ecstasy was much lower among younger pupils than it was among 15 year olds.

Over one third (36%) of pupils had at some point been offered at least one drug. Twenty eight per cent had been offered cannabis, 17% a 'stimulant' (a group of drugs which includes cocaine or ecstasy) and 6% heroin. There was a sharp increase with age in the numbers of young people exposed to drugs in this way. Sixty one per cent of pupils had been offered drugs by the age of 15, compared with only 15% who had had this experience by the age of 11.

Around one pupil in six (16%) reported that they had ever used one or more drugs and 14% had done so in the last year. Both figures represent fewer than half the number who had been offered drugs. Among 15 year olds, 32% of pupils had ever used drugs, 29% had used drugs in the last year and 21% had used drugs in the last month.

Cannabis was by far the most widely used drug. Twelve per cent reported use of this drug in the last year. Every other individual drug had been used in the last year by no more than 3%, with a total of 4% using any Class A drug in this period. By age 15 three in ten had used at least one drug in the last twelve months, nearly all of whom had used cannabis. Nine per cent had used at least one Class A drug, though the drugs that cause the most harm (cocaine and heroin) had respectively been used in the last year by only 2% and 1% of 15 year olds.

The 2000 figures for drug use were marginally above those recorded in the previous two years.

Health education (Chapter 11)

The proportion of pupils who remembered having lessons on smoking in the last 12 months had increased from 42% in 1986 to a peak of 78% in 1998 and in 2000 stood at 66%. Recall of lessons about alcohol followed a similar pattern, with 36% of pupils remembering a lesson about alcohol in 1988, 66% in 1998 and 58% in 2000. Lessons about drugs were remembered by 38% of pupils in 1988; this increased to 64% in 1996 and thereafter has remained at around this level.

There are two opposing views about giving pupils lessons on smoking, drinking or drug use. One view is that talking about these issues encourages experimentation, while the other is that ignorance of the issues means pupils experiment because they do not understand the potential consequences. This survey found no evidence that having lessons on smoking, drinking and drugs either encouraged or discouraged experimentation or use.

Smoking, drinking and drug use (Chapter 12)

Smoking, drinking and drug use were all highly interrelated behaviours. Pupils who smoked were more likely to drink, and pupils who drank were more likely to smoke. Similarly pupils who either drank or smoked were more likely to take drugs. There was a stronger relationship between smoking and drug taking than there was between smoking and drinking or between drinking and drug use. All three behaviours were strongly linked to age. Nevertheless, these relationships were evident even once the greater age of pupils who smoked, drank and/or used drugs was taken into account.

Social and educational factors (Chapter 13)

Pupils' social characteristics were related to smoking, drinking and drug use although the strength and direction of the relationships varied for different behaviours. Of the three behaviours, smoking has been shown (from this survey and others) to have the strongest relationship with social and educational characteristics. Prevalence of smoking was higher among those receiving free school meals (the main indicator of disadvantage collected in this survey). Drug use had a weaker relationship, with a slightly higher prevalence among those taking free school meals. In contrast, drinking showed no relationship with free school meals.

The type of school attended had a modest association with levels of smoking and drug use, but was not related to whether pupils drank alcohol. Pupils at the small number of secondary modern schools in the sample were slightly more likely to smoke and use drugs even once their age, sex, ethnicity and uptake of free school meals was taken into account, whilst pupils at private schools were slightly less likely to smoke.

Pupils who had played truant or had been excluded were more likely than those who had not to smoke, drink or take drugs, even once age differences had been taken into account.

Comparisons between England and Scotland (Chapter 14)

The age range of pupils surveyed was different in England and Scotland. Therefore in order to compare the two countries, analysis was restricted to those aged 12-15.

There was no difference in overall prevalence of regular smokers between England and Scotland, although among 15 year olds there were more regular smokers in England than in Scotland. Pupils in England were a little more likely to have drunk alcohol in the last week, but those who did drink consumed less than their counterparts in Scotland. There were no significant differences between England and Scotland in the proportions of pupils who used drugs in the last month or last year.

1 Introduction

Richard Boreham

1.1 Background to the 2000 survey

The Department of Health commissioned the National Centre for Social Research (NatCen) and the National Foundation for Educational Research (NFER) to conduct the 2000 survey of smoking, drinking and drug use among secondary school pupils in England. This survey is the latest in a series established in 1982 and which provides national estimates of the proportion of young people aged 11-15 who smoke, drink alcohol and/or take illegal drugs. An equivalent survey was also conducted in Scotland.

From 1982 to 1998, surveys were conducted biennially (with an additional survey in 1993). Initially, the survey covered cigarette smoking prevalence and smoking behaviour. In 1988 the focus was widened to include alcohol consumption. In 1998 questions about illegal drugs were introduced and since then the survey has been carried out annually. Core questions on smoking, drinking and drug use are asked every year, with alternate surveys focusing in more detail either on smoking and drinking, as in 2000, or on illegal drugs, as in 1999.

This long established series of surveys acts as an official measure of progress towards targets for reducing smoking and drug use among young people.

The current target for reducing children's smoking was set in *Smoking Kills, A White Paper on Tobacco*[1] and is measured against a 1996 baseline for 11-15 year olds. The target is:

- To reduce smoking among children from 13% to 9% or less by the year 2010, with a fall to 11% by the year 2005.

The Anti Drugs Co-ordinator's first annual report[2] contains targets for reducing drug use among young people. The other key performance indicators measured in part by this survey (against a 1999 baseline for 11-15 year olds) are:

- To reduce the proportion of people under the age of 25 reporting the use of Class A drugs by 25 per cent by 2005 (and by 50 per cent by 2008).

- To reduce the availability of Class A drugs by 25 per cent by 2005 (and by 50 per cent by 2008).

As well as monitoring overall prevalence of smoking, drinking and drug use, the survey also informs policy and practice by measuring further aspects of behaviour, knowledge and attitudes.

1.2 Sample design and response rates

The survey was conducted in schools by asking pre-selected groups of pupils to complete a confidential questionnaire and smoking diary. Both the schools and pupils were selected randomly in a way designed to give every eligible child in England the same chance of inclusion in the study.

The survey population (that is, the coverage of the survey) is pupils in school years 7-11 in England. Therefore, those taking part are mainly aged 11-15. Schools with any pupils in this age range are eligible for selection, with the exception of special schools. All other types, namely comprehensive, secondary modern, grammar and private schools, are included. Coverage was similar in Scotland, although among years S1-S4 and those taking part are mainly 12-15 year olds. More detail about the survey design can be found in Appendix A.

In total, 225 schools agreed to take part in the survey out of the 313 selected, a response rate of 72%. Field work was conducted in the autumn term of 2000. Approximately of 35 pupils per school were selected from across all classes in years 7 to 11 to take part. The response from selected pupils in participating schools was substantially higher, with 87% completing a questionnaire to yield a total of 7089 completed questionnaires. The product of these rates produces an overall response of 63%.

Figure 1.1

Response: 1982-2000

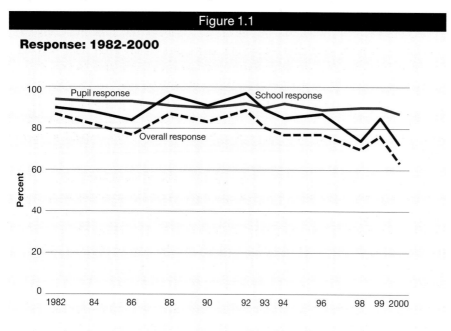

The most common reasons that schools gave for not wanting to take part were a lack of staff time and recent participation in other surveys, particularly surveys which covered smoking, drinking or drug use.

Response was lower in the following categories of schools:

- Private schools

- Schools with less than 750 pupils

- Schools with low levels of pupils with English as an alternative language

- Schools with low levels of pupils eligible for free school meals

- Schools with higher GSCE pass rates

Analysis was conducted to see whether there was any need for weighting to correct for the differential response rates (see Appendix A for details). Non-response weights made no difference to survey estimates and so weighting was not applied. The results from the 2000 survey are therefore comparable with those from previous surveys.

Full details of the survey design are included in Appendix A, and the main aspects of the design are outlined in this section:

- Pupils completed a questionnaire and smoking diary in exam conditions within one school period under the supervision of an interviewer

- If four or more pupils were absent a second visit to the school was under taken

Details of statistical analysis techniques used in this report are contained in Appendix B.

1.3 How reliable are children's answers?

Collecting information in school classrooms rather than homes, and repeated assurances of confidentiality, are key factors in encouraging honest reporting of behaviours which pupils may wish to conceal from adults or to exaggerate to their peers. Biochemical evidence from several previous surveys had indicated that pupils gave generally accurate answers about their smoking behaviour. Given this evidence, the decision was taken not to collect any biochemical evidence in 2000; nor were measures taken to test the truthfulness of reporting of drinking and drug use.

The earlier biochemical evidence was derived from saliva samples obtained between 1990 and 1998 from pupils in half the participating schools. Samples were tested for the presence of cotinine, which is a major metabolite of nicotine and reflects recent exposure to tobacco smoke, in order to validate the estimates of the prevalence of smoking derived from the questionnaire and diary. Results have consistently indicated that children are largely honest about their smoking – only a few children in each survey have had saliva cotinine levels that clearly contradicted their self-reported smoking behaviour.[3] In these previous surveys the results of saliva cotinine tests have not been used to re-classify the smoking behaviour of individual children (and if they had, prevalence rates would not have been altered).

It might be expected that the act of taking saliva samples during questionnaire completion would itself encourage pupils to be more honest, and therefore increase significantly the proportion of pupils reporting that they were smokers. However, this has not been the case; in the surveys in this series between 1990 and 1998 there have been no significant differences in smoking prevalence between the test and non-test halves of the samples. Hence, if there was any impact of omitting the saliva testing in 2000 it is highly likely to have been very small.

While there is no specific evidence on honesty in reporting drinking or drug use, it is assumed that the proven high level of honesty for smoking is matched for these substances.

Of course, honesty is not the only factor affecting the accuracy of responses. Accurately recalling levels of consumption of cigarettes or alcohol is not straightforward for children or adults. Uncertainty of recall accuracy is discussed in the relevant chapters.

1.4 Precision of estimates

As the data are based on a sample (rather than a census) of pupils, the estimates are subject to sampling error – Appendix A details how to calculate sampling errors for this survey.

Differences are generally commented upon only if they are significant at the 95% confidence level, implying no more than a 5% chance that any reported difference is not a real one but a consequence of sampling error.

In addition to sampling error, survey estimates are subject to other types of error or bias, including under-reporting or over-reporting of claimed behaviour and non-response bias. However, previous sections of this introduction and Appendix A describe a number of steps taken to limit and test potential sources of error in the data collected by this survey.

Notes and references

1 *Smoking Kills, A White Paper on Tobacco* (Cm 4177: Stationery Office, 1998).

2 *Tackling Drugs to Build a Better Britain. The Government's 10-year Strategy for Tackling Drug Misuse* (Cm 3945 London: The Stationery Office, 1998).

3 See Goddard & Higgins (1999) *Smoking, drinking and drug use among young teenagers in 1998* for a fuller discussion.

Table 1.1

Response rates: 1982-2000

England 1982-2000

Response	Survey year											
	1982	1984	1986	1988	1990	1992	1993	1994	1996	1998	1999	2000
	%	%	%	%	%	%	%	%	%	%	%	%
School	90	88	84	96	91	97	89	85	87	74	85	72
Pupil	94	93	93	91	90	92	90	92	89	90	90	87
Overall	87	82	77	87	83	89	80	77	77	70	76	63

2 Classification of smoking behaviour

Harriet Becher

2.1 Introduction

The self-completion questionnaire used in this series of surveys contains two questions – a 'prevalence' question (Q7) and a 'check' question (Q8) – designed to assess pupils' smoking status. In addition, pupils are asked to fill in a smoking diary, against which their previous answers are compared. These sources of information are used to classify pupils according to whether they are regular smokers (defined as usually smoking at least one cigarette a week), occasional smokers (defined as smoking less than one cigarette a week) or non-smokers. Those pupils who say at the prevalence questions that they are not smokers, but who record that they have smoked cigarettes in the diary, are reclassified in the analysis as occasional smokers (regardless of the number of cigarettes recorded).

Figure 2.1 Prevalence question (Q7) and check question (Q8)

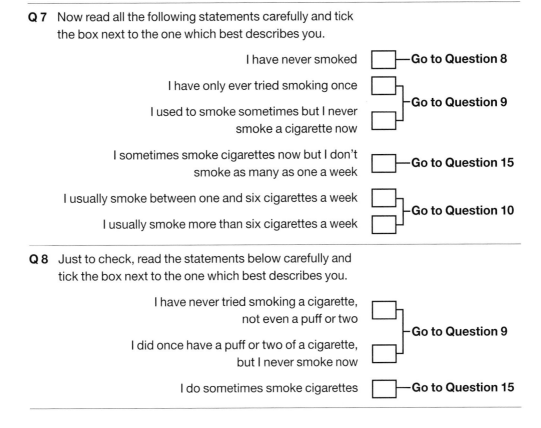

Q 7 Now read all the following statements carefully and tick the box next to the one which best describes you.

I have never smoked — Go to Question 8

I have only ever tried smoking once

I used to smoke sometimes but I never smoke a cigarette now — Go to Question 9

I sometimes smoke cigarettes now but I don't smoke as many as one a week — Go to Question 15

I usually smoke between one and six cigarettes a week

I usually smoke more than six cigarettes a week — Go to Question 10

Q 8 Just to check, read the statements below carefully and tick the box next to the one which best describes you.

I have never tried smoking a cigarette, not even a puff or two

I did once have a puff or two of a cigarette, but I never smoke now — Go to Question 9

I do sometimes smoke cigarettes — Go to Question 15

2.2 Smoking behaviour according to the questionnaire

The questionnaire assesses smoking status in two stages. Those pupils who say at the prevalence question that they have never smoked are then routed to the check question (see Figure 2.1). In each survey, a small proportion (6% in 2000) of those who initially say that they have never smoked admit at the check question that they have done so, and are therefore reclassified. Table 2.1 shows the effect of using this combined measure to classify smoking behaviour. The proportion of pupils saying that they had never smoked is reduced from 59% using the prevalence question alone to 55% using the prevalence and check questions combined. The proportion who admit to having experimented briefly with smoking cigarettes increases from 16% to 20%. Table 2.3 shows how the final smoking classification is assigned.

(Tables 2.1, 2.3, Figure 2.1)

2.3 Cigarettes smoked according to the diary

In addition to the questionnaire, pupils were asked to complete a diary for the previous seven days. Each day was divided into six sections: early morning, morning, dinner time, afternoon, teatime and evening. For each of the previous seven days, pupils were asked a question about what they had been doing at each time of day, and were asked to indicate how many cigarettes, if any, they had smoked. The diary was completed after the questionnaire, and regardless of what pupils had said about their smoking at the prevalence questions.

The purpose of the diary is to provide a better estimate of how many cigarettes children smoke than can be obtained by asking a direct question about their smoking behaviour. Table 2.2 shows the number of cigarettes recorded on the diary, compared with pupils' responses in the questionnaire. It should be noted that complete consistency between the questionnaire and the diary would not be expected, since the prevalence question asks about a pupil's 'usual' behaviour, while the diary refers to a specific week. Nevertheless, both regular and occasional smokers appear to have underestimated how much they smoked. Of those pupils who reported at the prevalence question that they usually smoked between one and six cigarettes a week, 73% recorded on the diary that they had smoked seven or more cigarettes in the past week. This underestimation does not affect their classification as regular smokers, since this depended only on their saying that they smoked at least one cigarette a week at the prevalence question.

However, this under-reporting is also present among occasional smokers (those who said at the prevalence question that they did smoke, but not as many as one a week). Nearly half (49%) of these had smoked between one and six cigarettes in the previous week, and a further 20% had apparently smoked seven or more cigarettes, on average at least one per day. That is, 69% of self-reported 'occasional' smokers in 2000 actually reported behaviour in the previous week that was consistent with the survey definition of regular smokers. Proportions have been similarly high in previous years. These children have not been reassigned to the 'regular smokers' group because of the possibility that their smoking behaviour during the previous week was not typical (this preserves continuity with previous surveys in the series).

This under-reporting of smoking behaviour is consistent with that observed in previous surveys in the series,[1] as well as in other surveys of smoking among adults.[2] It is likely that underestimation is, in most cases, not deliberate, but arises from the difficulty of the task of recalling the number of cigarettes smoked over a given period. In addition there may be a tendency to under-report 'unhealthy' behaviours such as cigarette smoking. It has also been suggested that the instability, experimentation and rapid change that is a feature of young people's lives means that some may find the concept of 'usual' behaviour referred to in the prevalence question difficult to grasp. As a consequence, some of the children classified in the survey as occasional smokers may actually resemble regular smokers according to the definition we are using.[3]

(Table 2.2)

Where children say at the prevalence question that they are non-smokers, but record cigarettes on the diary, they are reclassified as occasional smokers, regardless of the number of cigarettes recorded. Thus the use of the diary leads to a larger proportion of pupils classified as occasional smokers, but the proportion of pupils classified as regular smokers is not affected. The full classification of smoking behaviour, based on both the questionnaire and the diary, is shown in Table 2.3.

(Table 2.3)

Notes and references

1 Goddard E, Higgins V (1999) *Smoking, drinking and drug use among young teenagers in 1998* Stationery Office, London.

2 For an example see the comparison between saliva cotinine and self-reported smoking among adults discussed in Boreham, R (2001) *Use of tobacco products*, pp 97-120 in Eren B & Primatesta P *Health Survey for England: The Health of Minority Ethnic Groups '99*, (London: SO).

3 See Goddard, E and Higgins, V *Smoking, drinking and drug use among young teenagers in 1998: Volume 1: England*, 1999 (London: SO).

Table 2.1

Replies to smoking prevalence and check question[a]

All pupils   *England 2000*

	Prevalence question	Check question	Both questions combined
	%	%	%
I have never smoked	59	94	55
I have only smoked once	16	6	20
I used to smoke sometimes, but I never smoke now	9	0	9
I sometimes smoke cigarettes now, but I don't smoke as many as one a week	6	0	6
I usually smoke between one and six cigarettes a week	3	0	3
I usually smoke more than six cigarettes a week	7	0	7
Bases	*7061*	*4140*	*7061*

[a] See Figure 2.1 for details of these questions.

Table 2.2

Cigarettes recorded on the diary, by smoking behaviour according to the questionnaire

All pupils   *England 2000*

Total cigarettes on one-week diary	Usually smokes			Used to smoke	Tried smoking	Never smoked	Total
	More than 6 a week	1-6 a week	Less than 1 a week				
	%	%	%	%	%	%	%
None	0	2	31	85	94	99	83
1-6	0	25	49	11	4	0	6
7-70	70	69	19	3	1	1	9
71 or more	29	4	1	0	0	-	2
Bases[a]	*484*	*234*	*394*	*623*	*1326*	*3736*	*6797*

[a] This figure excludes 264 pupils who did not complete a smoking diary.

Table 2.3

Classification of smoking behaviour derived from the questionnaire and the diary

All pupils *England 2000*

Classification	Smoking prevalence and check questions	Diary	Number of pupils	%
Regular smoker	Usually smokes more than 6 cigs	Cigs	483	
	Usually smokes more than 6 cigs	No cigs	1	
	Usually smokes more than 6 cigs	Incomplete	9	
	Usually smokes 1-6 cigs	Cigs	229	10
	Usually smokes 1-6 cigs	No cigs	5	
	Usually smokes 1-6 cigs	Incomplete	5	
			732	
Occasional smoker	Smokes sometimes	Cigs	272	
	Smokes sometimes	No cigs	122	
	Smokes sometimes	Incomplete	13	
	Used to smoke	Cigs	92	9
	Tried smoking once	Cigs	78	
	Never smoked	Cigs	30	
			607	
Used to smoke	Used to smoke	No cigs	531	8
	Used to smoke	Incomplete	21	
Tried smoking once	Tried smoking once	No cigs	1248	19
	Tried smoking once	Incomplete	59	
Never smoked	Never smoked	No cigs	3706	55
	Never smoked	Incomplete	157	
Total			7061	

3 Smoking prevalence and cigarette consumption

Harriet Becher

3.1 Trends in cigarette smoking prevalence

The Government's target[1] is to reduce the number of children aged 11-15 who smoke regularly from a baseline of 13% in 1996 to 11% by 2005 and 9% by 2010. One of the aims of this survey is to measure progress towards this target.

The proportion of pupils who were regular smokers (defined as usually smoking at least one cigarette a week) had fallen from 13 per cent in 1996 to 9 per cent in 1999, but increased to 10 per cent in 2000. However, because of the fluctuations in smoking behaviour since 1982, it is not possible to tell whether this is the beginning of a new upward trend in cigarette smoking. **(Figure 3. 1)**

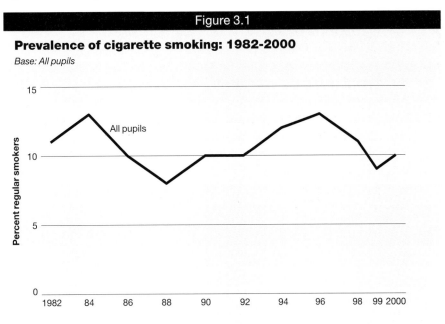

Figure 3.1

Prevalence of cigarette smoking: 1982-2000
Base: All pupils

As Figure 3.2 shows, there are clear differences in the prevalence of cigarette smoking between boys and girls. In the early 1980's, boys and girls were equally likely to smoke, but since then girls have been consistently more likely to smoke than boys. In 2000 12% of 11-15 year old girls were regular smokers, compared with 9% of boys. **(Table 3.1, Figure 3.2)**

3.2 Smoking behaviour in relation to sex, age and school year

Previous surveys have shown that the prevalence of smoking increases sharply with age and also with progress through the school (these two factors are of course closely linked). Of the two, age is more strongly related to cigarette smoking prevalence.

These patterns are repeated in the 2000 survey. Only 1% of 11 year olds in 2000 were regular smokers, and 80% had never even tried smoking. The numbers of children experimenting with smoking increased significantly for each age group, so that by the age

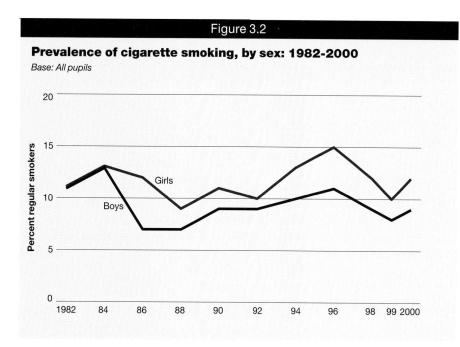

Figure 3.2

Prevalence of cigarette smoking, by sex: 1982-2000

Base: All pupils

of 15, around a quarter (23%) of pupils were regular smokers, with only 33% never having tried a cigarette.

The difference in smoking behaviour between boys and girls can be shown by looking at the proportions who are current or ex-smokers at each age, compared with the proportions who have never tried smoking, or who have only tried it once. There is no significant difference in smoking prevalence at ages 11 to 13 between boys and girls, although by age 13 gender differences in the proportions of current smokers begin to emerge. However, by age 14 more girls are in the current or ex-smokers category than boys (42% compared with 30%). The gap between girls and boys remains at age 15, so that more girls are current or ex-smokers than boys from age 14 upwards. This suggests that 13 and 14 are key ages for experimentation, since it is at this point that the gender difference emerges.

(Tables 3.2-3.5, Figure 3.3)

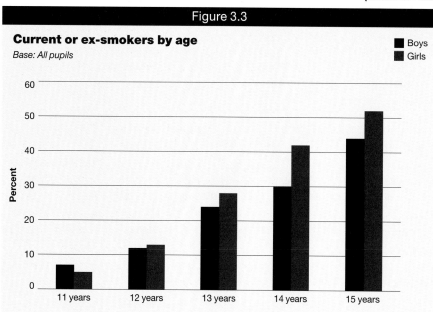

Figure 3.3

Current or ex-smokers by age

Base: All pupils

■ Boys
■ Girls

3.3 Smoking behaviour by ethnic group

In the 2000 questionnaire, pupils were asked to identify their ethnic group. As a result it is possible to look at differences in self-reported smoking behaviour between ethnic groups.

Although small base sizes for some groups make it difficult to draw reliable conclusions, some significant differences do emerge in the numbers who are current or ex-smokers, compared with those who have never tried, or who have only experimented briefly.

Girls who identify themselves as 'Black or Black British', as 'Other', and most notably as 'Asian or Asian British', are less likely to be current or ex-smokers than girls who identify themselves as 'White' or 'Mixed'. Among boys, however, there are no significant differences in smoking behaviour between these groups. In contrast to findings for the sample as a whole, among the Asian and Other groups, girls are less likely to be smokers than boys. These findings mirror those reported in other studies.[2]   **(Table 3.6)**

3.4 Cigarette consumption according to the diary

The numbers of cigarettes recorded on the diary as being smoked on each day of the previous week were added together to give a measure of cigarette consumption.

Since this series of surveys began in 1982, cigarette consumption among both boys and girls has remained relatively stable. The average number of cigarettes smoked per week by boys who were regular smokers has fluctuated in the low to mid 50s (apart from the 1998 figure of 65, which is probably a statistical 'blip'). The corresponding figure for girls has similarly fluctuated in the mid to high 40s. The mean number of cigarettes smoked overall per pupil (for all pupils, including non-smokers) has also remained fairly steady, at around five to seven cigarettes a week.   **(Table 3.7)**

Table 3.8 shows cigarette consumption for regular and occasional smokers in 2000. Twenty one per cent of regular smokers had smoked an average of 10 or more cigarettes per day in the last seven days, and further 35% had smoked an average of between 5 and 10 cigarettes per day. Only one percent of regular smokers had not smoked any cigarettes in the last seven days. As discussed in section 2.3, there was some discrepancy between the self-reported smoking habits of 'occasional' smokers, and the number of cigarettes recorded in the smoking diary – 21% of occasional smokers had not smoked any cigarettes, and 56% had smoked less than one cigarette a day on average. However 23% of self-reported occasional smokers had smoked at least one cigarette a day on average over the last 7 days.

In addition, Table 3.8 shows the mean numbers of cigarettes recorded on the diary by regular and occasional smokers. The median number of cigarettes is also given, since a few pupils recorded a large number of cigarettes on the diary, distorting the mean value. A very small number of pupils (6 in England) were judged to have entered an unrealistically high value on the diary – data from these pupils is not included. With this exception, these figures are based on all smokers, including those who recorded no cigarettes on the diary. Unsurprisingly, both mean and median consumption were much higher for regular smokers (mean 46 cigarettes, median 40) than for occasional smokers (mean 7 cigarettes, median 2). Among regular smokers, consumption was higher for boys than for girls.   **(Table 3.8)**

Notes and references

1 The government's smoking strategy is set out in *Smoking Kills: A White Paper on Tobacco*, Cm 4177, Stationery Office (1998).

2   Nazroo J, Becher H, Kelly Y & McMunn A (2001) *Children's health* in Erens B & Primatesta P (eds) *Health Survey for England: The Health of Minority Ethnic Groups '99*, (London: SO).

Table 3.1

Smoking behaviour, by sex: 1982 to 2000

All pupils   *England 1982-2000*

Smoking behaviour	Year										
	1982	1984	1986	1988	1990	1992	1994	1996	1998	1999	2000
	%	%	%	%	%	%	%	%	%	%	%
Boys											
Regular smoker	11	13	7	7	9	9	10	11	9	8	9
Occasional smoker	7	9	5	5	6	6	9	8	8	4	7
Used to smoke	11	11	10	8	7	6	7	7	9	9	8
Tried smoking	26	24	23	23	22	22	21	22	20	22	20
Never smoked	45	44	55	58	56	57	53	53	54	57	56
Girls											
Regular smoker	11	13	12	9	11	10	13	15	12	10	12
Occasional smoker	9	9	5	5	6	7	10	10	8	6	10
Used to smoke	10	10	10	9	7	7	8	9	10	11	8
Tried smoking	22	22	19	19	18	19	17	18	18	18	17
Never smoked	49	46	53	59	58	57	52	48	51	55	53
Total											
Regular smoker	11	13	10	8	10	10	12	13	11	9	10
Occasional smoker	8	9	5	5	6	7	9	9	8	5	9
Used to smoke	10	10	10	8	7	7	8	8	10	10	8
Tried smoking	24	23	21	21	20	20	19	20	19	20	19
Never smoked	47	45	54	58	57	57	53	51	53	56	55
Bases											
Boys	*1460*	*1928*	*1676*	*1489*	*1643*	*1662*	*1522*	*1445*	*2311*	*4791*	*3654*
Girls	*1514*	*1689*	*1508*	*1529*	*1478*	*1626*	*1523*	*1409*	*2413*	*4542*	*3407*
Total	*2979*	*3658*	*3189*	*3018*	*3121*	*3295*	*3045*	*2854*	*4723*	*9333*	*7061*

Table 3.2

Smoking behaviour, by sex and age

All pupils   *England 2000*

Smoking behaviour	Age					
	11 years	12 years	13 years	14 years	15 years	Total
	%	%	%	%	%	%
Boys						
Regular smoker	1	2	6	11	21	9
Occasional smoker	5	4	8	9	11	7
Used to smoke	2	6	9	11	12	8
Current or ex-smoker	*7*	*12*	*24*	*30*	*44*	*24*
Tried smoking	13	20	18	25	22	20
Never smoked	80	68	59	44	34	56
Tried once or never smoked	*93*	*88*	*76*	*70*	*56*	*76*
Girls						
Regular smoker	1	2	10	19	26	12
Occasional smoker	3	6	12	13	14	10
Used to smoke	2	5	7	10	12	8
Current or ex-smoker	*5*	*13*	*28*	*42*	*52*	*29*
Tried smoking	14	15	20	20	16	17
Never smoked	81	72	52	38	32	53
Tried once or never smoked	*95*	*87*	*72*	*58*	*48*	*71*
Total						
Regular smoker	1	2	8	15	23	10
Occasional smoker	4	5	10	11	12	9
Used to smoke	2	6	8	10	12	8
Current or ex-smoker	*6*	*13*	*26*	*36*	*48*	*27*
Tried smoking	13	17	19	23	19	19
Never smoked	80	70	56	41	33	55
Tried once or never smoked	*94*	*87*	*74*	*64*	*52*	*73*
Bases						
Boys	*618*	*751*	*736*	*752*	*797*	*3654*
Girls	*572*	*686*	*697*	*688*	*764*	*3407*
Total	*1190*	*1437*	*1433*	*1440*	*1561*	*7061*

Table 3.3

Smoking behaviour, by sex and school year

All pupils   *England 2000*

Smoking behaviour	School Year					
	Y7	Y8	Y9	Y10	Y11	Total
	%	%	%	%	%	%
Boys						
Regular smoker	1	2	7	13	22	9
Occasional smoker	4	5	8	9	11	7
Used to smoke	3	6	10	11	12	8
Current or ex-smoker	*8*	*14*	*25*	*32*	*45*	*24*
Tried smoking	13	21	18	26	21	20
Never smoked	79	65	57	41	34	56
Tried once or never smoked	*92*	*86*	*75*	*68*	*55*	*76*
Girls						
Regular smoker	0	3	11	21	26	12
Occasional smoker	3	6	13	14	13	10
Used to smoke	2	5	8	11	12	8
Current or ex-smoker	*5*	*15*	*31*	*45*	*52*	*29*
Tried smoking	14	16	19	19	17	17
Never smoked	81	69	50	36	31	53
Tried once or never smoked	*95*	*85*	*69*	*55*	*48*	*71*
Total						
Regular smoker	1	3	9	17	24	10
Occasional smoker	3	6	10	11	12	9
Used to smoke	2	5	9	11	12	8
Current or ex-smoker	*7*	*14*	*28*	*39*	*48*	*27*
Tried smoking	13	19	19	23	19	19
Never smoked	80	67	54	39	33	55
Tried once or never smoked	*93*	*86*	*72*	*61*	*52*	*73*
Bases						
Boys	*750*	*746*	*748*	*732*	*678*	*3654*
Girls	*665*	*709*	*689*	*701*	*643*	*3407*
Total	*1415*	*1455*	*1437*	*1433*	*1321*	*7061*

Table 3.4

Proportion of pupils who were regular smokers, by sex and age: 1982 to 2000

All pupils   *England 1982-2000*

Age	Year											
	1982	1984	1986	1988	1990	1992	1994	1996	1998	1999	2000	*2000 Bases*
	Pecentage who were regular smokers											
Boys												
11 years	1	0	0	0	0	0	1	1	1	1	1	*618*
12 years	2	2	2	2	2	2	2	2	3	2	2	*751*
13 years	8	10	5	5	6	6	4	8	5	4	6	*736*
14 years	18	16	6	8	10	14	14	13	15	10	11	*752*
15 years	24	28	18	17	25	21	26	28	19	21	21	*797*
Total	11	13	7	7	9	9	10	11	9	8	9	*3654*
Girls												
11 years	0	1	0	1	1	0	0	0	1	0	1	*572*
12 years	1	2	2	0	2	2	3	4	3	3	2	*686*
13 years	6	9	5	4	9	9	8	11	9	8	10	*697*
14 years	14	19	16	12	16	15	20	24	19	15	19	*688*
15 years	25	28	27	22	25	25	30	33	29	25	26	*764*
Total	11	13	12	9	11	10	13	15	12	10	12	*3407*
All pupils												
11 years	a	a	a	a	a	a	a	1	1	1	1	*1190*
12 years	a	a	a	a	a	a	a	3	4	3	2	*1437*
13 years	a	a	a	a	a	a	a	10	8	6	8	*1433*
14 years	a	a	a	a	a	a	a	18	19	12	15	*1440*
15 years	a	a	a	a	a	a	a	30	24	23	23	*1561*
Total	a	a	a	a	a	a	a	13	11	9	10	*7061*

a Data was not published for all pupils prior to 1996.

Table 3.5

Proportion of pupils who were regular smokers, by sex and school year: 1982 to 2000

All pupils   *England 1982-2000*

School year	Year											
	1982	1984	1986	1988	1990	1992	1994	1996	1998	1999	2000	*2000 Bases*
	%	%	%	%	%	%	%	%	%	%	%	*%*
Boys												
Y 7	3	0	0	1	1	1	2	1	1	1	1	*750*
Y 8	2	3	2	2	3	3	2	4	3	2	2	*746*
Y 9	9	12	5	5	7	7	5	8	5	5	7	*748*
Y 10	19	17	8	9	12	16	15	13	17	12	13	*732*
Y 11	26	31	19	18	26	20	28	28	20	22	22	*678*
Total	11	13	7	7	9	9	10	11	9	8	9	*3654*
Girls												
Y 7	0	1	0	0	1	1	1	1	1	1	0	*665*
Y 8	2	2	2	0	4	3	3	4	4	4	3	*709*
Y 9	7	9	6	5	10	10	10	13	10	8	11	*689*
Y 10	15	24	18	13	15	17	23	24	21	16	21	*701*
Y 11	28	28	30	23	27	25	30	34	29	26	26	*643*
Total	11	13	12	9	11	10	13	15	12	10	12	*3407*
All pupils												
Y 7	a	a	a	a	a	a	a	a	1	1	1	*1415*
Y 8	a	a	a	a	a	a	a	a	4	3	3	*1455*
Y 9	a	a	a	a	a	a	a	a	8	7	9	*1437*
Y 10	a	a	a	a	a	a	a	a	19	14	17	*1433*
Y 11	a	a	a	a	a	a	a	a	24	23	24	*1321*
Total	a	a	a	a	a	a	a	a	11	9	10	*7061*

[a] Data was not published for all pupils prior to 1998.

Table 3.6

Smoking behaviour, by sex and ethnic group

All pupils   *England 2000*

Smoking behaviour	Ethnic group					
	White	Mixed	Asian[a]	Black[b]	Other[c]	Total
	%	%	%	%	%	%
Boys						
Regular smoker	9	9	7	7	7	9
Occasional smoker	8	8	5	9	7	8
Used to smoke	8	13	9	7	4	8
Current or ex-smoker	*25*	*30*	*20*	*24*	*18*	*24*
Tried smoking	20	22	17	24	21	20
Never smoked	56	48	62	52	62	56
Tried once or never smoked	*75*	*70*	*80*	*76*	*82*	*76*
Girls						
Regular smoker	13	13	2	4	7	12
Occasional smoker	10	13	5	11	7	10
Used to smoke	8	8	2	7	3	8
Current or ex-smoker	*32*	*34*	*9*	*21*	*16*	*30*
Tried smoking	17	23	15	22	21	17
Never smoked	52	43	76	56	62	53
Tried once or never smoked	*68*	*66*	*91*	*79*	*84*	*70*
Total						
Regular smoker	11	11	4	6	7	10
Occasional smoker	9	10	5	10	7	9
Used to smoke	8	10	6	7	4	8
Current or ex-smoker	*28*	*32*	*15*	*23*	*17*	*27*
Tried smoking	18	23	17	23	21	18
Never smoked	54	45	69	54	62	55
Tried once or never smoked	*72*	*68*	*85*	*77*	*83*	*73*
Bases						
Boys	*3040*	*158*	*263*	*96*	*73*	*3630*
Girls	*2840*	*152*	*239*	*85*	*61*	*3377*
Total	*5880*	*310*	*502*	*181*	*134*	*7007*

[a] The full option given on the questionnaire was 'Asian or Asian British'.

[b] The full option given on the questionnaire was 'Black or Black British'.

[c] This also includes a few pupils who identified themselves as Chinese, as numbers were insufficient for a separate column.

Table 3.7

Mean and median cigarette consumption in the diary week, by sex: 1982 to 2000

All pupils   *England 1982-2000*

	Year									
	1982	1984	1986	1988	1990	1992	1994	1996	1998	2000
	%	%	%	%	%	%	%	%	%	%
Boys										
Regular smokers										
Mean	50	49	53	52	56	58	54	56	65	50
Median	40	40	43	49	48	51	44	46	55	43
Occasional smokers										
Mean	7	5	5	7	7	6	7	8	11	7
Median	2	1	1	3	3	1	2	3	2	2
Mean consumption per pupil (for all pupils)	6	7	4	4	6	5	6	7	7	5
Girls										
Regular smokers										
Mean	44	49	45	41	49	44	47	47	49	44
Median	36	38	36	38	40	34	37	40	41	36
Occasional smokers										
Mean	4	4	4	4	4	3	3	5	6	6
Median	1	2	1	1	2	1	2	2	2	2
Mean consumption per pupil (for all pupils)	5	7	6	4	5	4	6	8	6	6
Total										
Regular smokers										
Mean	47	49	48	46	53	51	50	51	56	46
Median	38	39	38	41	43	42	39	44	46	40
Occasional smokers										
Mean	6	4	5	6	6	5	5	7	8	7
Median	1	1	1	1	2	1	2	2	2	2
Mean consumption per pupil (for all pupils)	6	7	5	4	6	5	6	7	7	5
Bases										
Boys										
Regular smokers	*166*	*251*	*123*	*107*	*148*	*134*	*147*	*154*	*207*	*304*
Occasional smokers	*106*	*168*	*88*	*70*	*98*	*96*	*138*	*107*	*174*	*262*
All pupils	*1460*	*1928*	*1676*	*1488*	*1640*	*1641*	*1515*	*1442*	*2311*	*3475*
Girls										
Regular smokers	*159*	*221*	*183*	*136*	*158*	*147*	*200*	*208*	*295*	*409*
Occasional smokers	*130*	*152*	*82*	*76*	*90*	*96*	*143*	*141*	*201*	*332*
All pupils	*1514*	*1689*	*1508*	*1529*	*1478*	*1597*	*1521*	*1408*	*2413*	*3317*
Total										
Regular smokers	*326*	*474*	*306*	*246*	*306*	*281*	*347*	*362*	*502*	*713*
Occasional smokers	*236*	*324*	*170*	*148*	*188*	*192*	*281*	*248*	*375*	*594*
All pupils	*2979*	*3658*	*3189*	*3017*	*3118*	*3245*	*3036*	*2850*	*4723*	*6792*

Table 3.8

Number of cigarettes smoked in the diary week by current smokers, by sex

Current smokers   *England 2000*

Cigarette consumption in the diary week	Sex		
	Boys	Girls	Total
	%	%	%
Regular smokers			
None	1	1	1
Less than 7 a week	7	10	9
7, less than 14 a week	11	12	12
14, less than 21 a week	10	9	9
21, less than 35 a week	12	16	14
35, less than 70 a week	34	35	35
70 a week or more	25	17	21
Mean	50	44	46
Median	43	36	40
Occasional smokers			
None	19	22	21
Less than 7 a week	54	58	56
7, less than 14 a week	13	9	11
14, less than 21 a week	4	4	4
21, less than 35 a week	6	4	5
35, less than 70 a week	3	2	3
70 a week or more	1	1	1
Mean	7	6	7
Median	2	2	2
All current smokers			
None	9	10	10
Less than 7 a week	29	31	30
7, less than 14 a week	12	11	11
14, less than 21 a week	7	7	7
21, less than 35 a week	9	10	10
35, less than 70 a week	20	20	20
70 a week or more	14	10	12
Mean	30	27	28
Median	14	12	12
Bases			
Regular smokers	*304*	*409*	*713*
Occasional smokers	*262*	*332*	*594*
All current smokers	*566*	*741*	*1307*

4 Dependence on smoking and family attitudes towards smoking

Harriet Becher

4.1 Introduction

Regular smokers were asked a series of questions intended to assess the extent to which they were dependent on smoking. These questions were first introduced in England in 1994, and cover how easy or difficult pupils think it would be to go without smoking for a week; how easy or difficult they think it would be to give up altogether; whether pupils would like to give up altogether, and whether they have ever actually tried to give up smoking. In addition, since 1988 pupils have been asked how long it has been since they started smoking at least one cigarette a week, to provide an indication of the length of time for which they have been a regular smoker.

The relatively small numbers of pupils who were regular smokers precludes very accurate comparisons between boys and girls, or between pupils of different ages. Therefore, unless there is a substantial difference between any of these groups, this chapter will focus on all regular smokers.

4.2 Changes over time in dependence on smoking

In 2000 over half of pupils questioned (58%) said they had been smoking regularly for more than one year. This is lower than the figures recorded in 1996 and 1998 (67% and 65% respectively).

The proportion of pupils who thought that they would find it difficult to go without smoking for a week has remained stable over time, at 58% (with an apparent 'blip' of 65% in 1996). The figure in 2000 was 58%. Similarly the proportion saying they would find it difficult to give up smoking altogether has hovered at between 70% and 75%, and was 73% in 2000.

Among regular smokers, the proportion who say they would like to give up altogether has fluctuated over time with no clear trend, and stood at 39% in 2000. The fact that this latter measure does not include those pupils who tried to give up and succeeded (and are therefore no longer in the 'regular smokers' group) makes it less reliable than the other measures of dependency used, and may explain the extent of the fluctuation. Furthermore, given that a much higher proportion have tried to give up than would like to give up (66% compared with 39%), it is difficult to say exactly what this question is measuring. However, the fact that so many current smokers have tried unsuccessfully to give up is consistent with what is known about adult smokers.[1]   **(Tables 4.1-4.4)**

4.3 Dependence on smoking by smoking behaviour

The length of time that pupils had been a regular smoker affected their attitudes towards giving up smoking. Compared with pupils who had been a regular smoker for one year or less, those who had been a regular smoker for longer were more likely to say that they would find it difficult not to smoke for a week (72% compared with 39%) and more likely to find it difficult to give up smoking altogether (83% compared with 58%). Smokers who had been smoking for longer were more likely to have tried to give up in the past and failed (73%) than those who had been a regular smoker for one year or less (57%). Despite their perceived greater dependence on cigarettes, smokers who had been smoking regularly for more than a year were keener to give up – 42% would like to stop smoking compared with 34% of smokers who had been a regular smoker for less time.　　　　**(Table 4.6, Figure 4.1)**

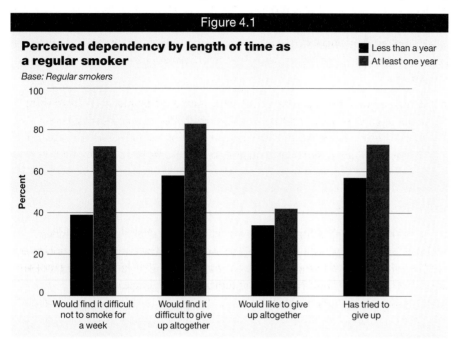

Figure 4.1

Perceived dependency by length of time as a regular smoker

■ Less than a year
■ At least one year

Base: Regular smokers

The number of cigarettes smoked in the last seven days was used to classify regular smokers into 'heavy' (10 or more cigarettes a day on average), 'medium' (3 or more, but less than 10 cigarettes a day on average) or 'light' (less than 3 cigarettes a day), in order to examine the relationship between number of cigarettes smoked and dependence. Even among light smokers there was evidence that pupils were dependent on cigarettes; 28% of light smokers would find it difficult not to smoke for a week, and 46% of light smokers would find it difficult to give up smoking altogether.

The more cigarettes pupils smoked, the greater their perceptions of their own dependence on cigarettes. Pupils who were classified as medium smokers were much more likely to feel dependent than light smokers. Heavy smokers perceived themselves as the most dependent, but the difference between them and medium smokers was not as great as the difference between medium and light smokers. Eighty seven percent of heavy smokers would find it difficult not to smoke for a week, compared with 65% of medium smokers and 28% of light smokers. There was a similar pattern in terms of whether pupils would find it difficult to give up smoking altogether, 92% of heavy smokers would find it difficult compared with 81% of medium smokers and 46% of light smokers.

Although pupils who smoked more cigarettes felt themselves to be more dependent, the proportion of regular smokers who wanted to give up increased from 33% of light smokers to 46% of heavy smokers.　　　　**(Table 4.7)**

Pupils who were more dependent on cigarettes, either through length of time smoking or through heavier levels of smoking, were more likely to have tried to give up than their less dependent counterparts. However, the fact that pupils had tried to give up and had failed did not deter them from wanting to give up. Regular smokers who had already tried to stop smoking were three times as likely as those who had not already tried, to say that they would like to give up (50% compared with 17%).　　　　**(Table 4.5)**

4.4　Attitudes of the family towards pupils' smoking

All pupils, regardless of their smoking status, were asked about their own family's attitudes to smoking. Although questions referred to the feelings of the family, it is likely that children were thinking mainly of their parents when they answered them. Self-reported non-smokers (including some who were later reclassified as occasional smokers because they had recorded some cigarettes on the diary) were asked how they thought their family would feel if they started smoking. Occasional and regular smokers were asked how their family felt about their smoking. Smokers who replied at this question that their family did not know they smoked (55% in 2000) were then asked how they thought their family would feel if they knew that they smoked. The answer categories corresponded, so it is possible to compare perceived parental attitudes towards smoking for non-smokers, occasional smokers and regular smokers.

Where pupils answered that their parents would either stop them smoking or would try to persuade them not to smoke, family attitudes can be interpreted as negative towards smoking. For those pupils who said they didn't know how their family would feel, we can infer that their family's attitude may be fairly neutral, since parents have apparently not expressed any feelings to the child either way. Meanwhile, those pupils who said that their parents did not mind, or that their family would encourage them, can be taken to have families with positive attitudes towards smoking.

The main message is that family attitudes are perceived as overwhelmingly negative towards smoking: 88% of pupils said that their parents would either stop them smoking or try to persuade them not to. Non-smokers were the most likely (90%) and regular smokers the least likely (75%) to report negative family attitudes. Regular smokers were correspondingly more likely than non-smokers to say that their parents were either neutral or positive towards smoking. Even so, negative family attitudes appeared to be the norm regardless of smoking status.

Among those children who said that their parents were negative towards smoking, distinctions can be drawn between whether their parents would actively stop them smoking, or whether they would take the milder option of trying to persuade them not to smoke. Non-smokers were more likely to say that their parents would stop them (65%) than to say their parents would attempt to persuade them not to smoke (25%). There was a similar pattern for occasional smokers although the pattern was less pronounced (43% compared with 38%) and among regular smokers the pattern was reversed with parents of regular smokers being less likely to stop their children smoking (21%) than to persuade them (54%).   **(Table 4.8)**

Among current smokers, it is possible to distinguish between 'open' smokers, whose parents knew that they smoked, and 'secret' smokers, who said their parents did not know about their smoking. This latter group answered the more hypothetical question about how they thought their family would feel if they knew the pupil smoked. Open smokers were less likely to say their parents would stop them from smoking, and more likely to say their parents would try to persuade them not to smoke or wouldn't mind, than secret smokers. Occasional smokers were more likely to belong to the secret smoker group. For this reason it could be argued that the differences in perceived parental attitude between regular and occasional smokers are explained by the differences between open and secret smokers. However, if we look at the two groups separately, it is clear that among both the open and secret smokers the same pattern of differences exists. That is, regular smokers are less likely than occasional smokers to say their parents would actively stop them smoking, regardless of whether their parents actually know that they smoke.   **(Table 4.9)**

The proportions of children reporting negative family attitudes were similar across age bands. However, there were differences in the type of negative attitude reported. Younger children were more likely than older children to say that their parents would stop them smoking; among non-smokers 72% of 11 year olds and 53% of 15 year olds said that their parents would stop them smoking. There was a similar age gradient among smokers although the proportions saying that their parents would stop them smoking were lower than among non-smokers (43% of 11 year olds compared with 25% of 15 year olds).
                                                                                       (Table 4.10)
Previous surveys in this series have also suggested that perceived family attitudes are related to both smoking status and age.[2] Since the two factors are themselves strongly related, it is difficult to tell whether both contribute to parental attitude, or whether one

factor is responsible. For example, it is possible that the differences in parental attitude observed between smokers and non-smokers are because smokers tend to be older, rather than being due to cigarette smoking status per se.

Looking at perceived family attitude by age-standardised smoking status allows us to assess the individual effects of both factors, as shown in Table 4.11. After the age profiles of each group are taken into account the differences between regular, occasional and non-smokers remain. The implication is that differences in perceived parental attitude are primarily explained by smoking status, and that age makes much less difference. Regular smokers who report that their parents are negative towards smoking are less likely to say that their parents would actively stop them smoking, and more likely to say that their parents would just try to persuade them not to smoke, than occasional or non-smokers. However, the direction of causality is not clear – that is, whether perceived parental attitude affects smoking behaviour, or whether smoking behaviour has an influence on parental attitude. **(Table 4.11, Figure 4.2)**

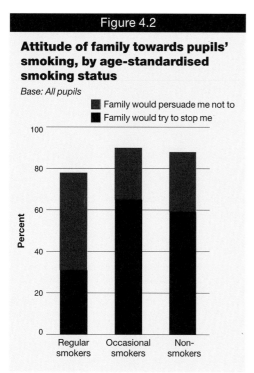

Figure 4.2

Attitude of family towards pupils' smoking, by age-standardised smoking status

Base: All pupils

■ Family would persuade me not to
■ Family would try to stop me

Notes and references

1 For discussion see Lader, D and Meltzer, H *Smoking Related Behaviour and Attitudes* 1999 (London: Office for National Statistics).

2 See Goddard, E and Higgins, V *Smoking, drinking and drug use among young teenagers in 1998: Volume 1: England*, 1999 (London: SO).

Table 4.1

Length of time as a regular smoker, by sex: 1988 to 2000

Regular smokers   *England 1988-2000*

Length of time as a regular smoker	Year						
	1988	1990	1992	1994	1996	1998	2000
	%	%	%	%	%	%	%
Boys							
Less than 3 months	11	8	17	13	7	10	12
3-6 months	14	14	14	8	5	5	9
6 months to 1 year	21	16	12	19	19	18	16
More than 1 year	54	62	57	61	69	67	63
Girls							
Less than 3 months	10	11	11	11	10	10	8
3-6 months	11	13	18	13	9	8	16
6 months to 1 year	21	23	14	22	16	18	22
More than 1 year	57	53	57	54	65	64	54
Total							
Less than 3 months	11	9	14	12	9	10	10
3-6 months	13	14	16	11	7	6	13
6 months to 1 year	21	19	13	20	18	18	19
More than 1 year	55	58	57	57	67	65	58
Bases							
Boys	*106*	*146*	*143*	*150*	*150*	*198*	*303*
Girls	*134*	*153*	*162*	*195*	*198*	*277*	*385*
Total	*243*	*299*	*305*	*345*	*348*	*475*	*688*

Table 4.2

Whether regular smokers would find it easy or difficult not to smoke for a week, by sex: 1994 to 2000

Regular smokers   *England 1994-2000*

Difficulty or ease of not smoking for a week	Year			
	1994	1996	1998	2000
	%	%	%	%
Boys				
Very difficult	19	33	31	25
Fairly difficult	34	33	23	34
Very or fairly difficult	*54*	*66*	*54*	*59*
Fairly easy	30	24	29	28
Very easy	16	10	17	13
Very or fairly easy	*46*	*34*	*46*	*41*
Girls				
Very difficult	24	31	28	25
Fairly difficult	37	33	32	32
Very or fairly difficult	*61*	*64*	*60*	*58*
Fairly easy	27	26	29	32
Very easy	12	10	11	10
Very or fairly easy	*39*	*36*	*40*	*42*
Total				
Very difficult	22	32	29	25
Fairly difficult	36	33	28	33
Very or fairly difficult	*58*	*65*	*58*	*58*
Fairly easy	28	25	29	30
Very easy	14	10	13	11
Very or fairly easy	*42*	*35*	*42*	*42*
Bases		.		
Boys	*148*	*150*	*199*	*305*
Girls	*195*	*199*	*276*	*385*
Total	*343*	*349*	*475*	*690*

Table 4.3

Whether regular smokers would find it easy or difficult to give up smoking altogether, by sex: 1994 to 2000

Regular smokers   *England 1994-2000*

Difficulty or ease of giving up altogether	Year			
	1994	1996	1998	2000
	%	%	%	%
Boys				
Very difficult	30	43	37	34
Fairly difficult	36	33	30	38
Very or fairly difficult	*66*	*76*	*67*	*72*
Fairly easy	22	17	25	18
Very easy	12	7	8	10
Very or fairly easy	*34*	*24*	*33*	*28*
Girls				
Very difficult	38	44	36	37
Fairly difficult	35	31	38	36
Very or fairly difficult	*73*	*75*	*74*	*73*
Fairly easy	20	21	21	21
Very easy	7	5	5	6
Very or fairly easy	*27*	*25*	*26*	*27*
Total				
Very difficult	35	44	36	36
Fairly difficult	35	32	35	37
Very or fairly difficult	*70*	*75*	*72*	*73*
Fairly easy	21	19	22	20
Very easy	9	6	6	7
Very or fairly easy	*30*	*25*	*29*	*27*
Bases				
Boys	*148*	*150*	*199*	*303*
Girls	*195*	*199*	*276*	*386*
Total	*343*	*349*	*475*	*689*

Table 4.4

Whether regular smokers a) would like to give up smoking altogether and b) have ever tried to give up smoking, by sex: 1994 to 2000

Regular smokers   *England 1994-2000*

	Year			
	1994	1996	1998	2000
	%	%	%	%
Boys				
Would like to give up				
Yes	36	45	38	37
No	20	21	22	14
Don't know	44	33	40	49
% Who have tried to give up	52	67	69	62
Girls				
Would like to give up				
Yes	33	44	32	41
No	18	9	16	15
Don't know	49	47	52	44
% Who have tried to give up	70	80	74	69
Total				
Would like to give up				
Yes	34	45	35	39
No	19	14	18	15
Don't know	47	41	47	46
% Who have tried to give up	62	75	72	66
Bases				
Boys	*149*	*150*	*199*	*304*
Girls	*195*	*199*	*277*	*386*
Total	*344*	*349*	*476*	*690*

Table 4.5

Whether regular smokers would like to give up smoking, by sex and whether they have tried

Regular smokers   *England 2000*

Whether would like to give up	Whether has ever tried tried to give up		
	Yes	No	Total
	%	%	%
Boys			
Yes	49	16	37
No	10	22	14
Don't know	41	62	49
Girls			
Yes	51	18	41
No	11	24	15
Don't know	38	58	44
Total			
Yes	50	17	39
No	10	23	15
Don't know	39	60	46
Bases			
Boys	*188*	*116*	*304*
Girls	*267*	*119*	*386*
Total	*455*	*235*	*690*

Table 4.6

Perceived dependency on smoking, by sex and length of time as a regular smoker

Regular smokers   *England 2000*

Dependency	Length of time as a smoker		
	1 year or less	More than 1 year	Total
	%	%	%
Boys			
Would find it difficult not to smoke for a week	37	71	59
Would find it difficult to give up altogether	55	82	72
Would like to give up altogether	28	41	37
Has tried to give up	51	68	62
Girls			
Would find it difficult not to smoke for a week	40	73	58
Would find it difficult to give up altogether	60	84	73
Would like to give up altogether	38	43	41
Has tried to give up	60	77	69
Total			
Would find it difficult not to smoke for a week	39	72	58
Would find it difficult to give up altogether	58	83	73
Would like to give up altogether	34	42	39
Has tried to give up	57	73	66
Bases			
Boys	*110*	*191*	*301*
Girls	*179*	*205*	*384*
Total	*289*	*396*	*685*

Table 4.7

Perceived dependency on smoking, by number of cigarettes smoked in the previous seven days

Regular smokers   *England 2000*

Dependency	Number of cigarettes smoked			
	0-20	21-70	71 or more	Total
	%	%	%	%
Would find it difficult not to smoke for a week	28	65	87	58
Would find it difficult to give up altogether	46	81	92	73
Would like to give up altogether	33	39	46	39
Has tried to give up	55	69	74	66
Bases	*203*	*327*	*140*	*670*

Table 4.8

Perceived attitude of family towards their child smoking, by sex and smoking behaviour

Regular smokers   *England 2000*

Attitude or expected attitude of family	Smoking status			
	Regular smokers	Occasional smokers	Non-smokers	Total
	%	%	%	%
Boys				
Family:				
Stop me	20	46	66	61
Persuade me not to	56	33	24	27
Don't mind	11	3	1	2
Encourage me	1	0	-	0
Not sure	12	17	9	10
Girls				
Family:				
Stop me	21	41	64	57
Persuade me not to	53	42	26	31
Don't mind	14	3	1	2
Encourage me	0	1	-	0
Not sure	12	14	9	10
Total				
Family:				
Stop me	21	43	65	59
Persuade me not to	54	38	25	29
Don't mind	13	3	1	2
Encourage me	1	1	-	0
Not sure	12	15	9	10
Bases				
Boys	*319*	*272*	*3052*	*3643*
Girls	*413*	*334*	*2652*	*3399*
Total	*732*	*606*	*5704*	*7042*

Table 4.9

Perceived attitude of family towards their child smoking, by smoking behaviour and whether or not family know the pupil smokes

Current smokers   *England 2000*

Attitude or expected attitude of family	'Open' smokers			'Secret' smokers		
	Regular smokers	Occasional smokers	All open smokers	Regular smokers	Occasional smokers	All secret smokers
	%	%	%	%	%	%
Family:						
Stop me	5	13	7	41	51	46
Persuade me not to	61	51	59	49	36	43
Don't mind	22	11	20	2	1	1
Encourage me	1	1	1	0	-	0
Not sure	11	24	14	8	12	10
Bases	*398*	*104*	*502*	*319*	*294*	*613*

Table 4.10

Family attitude to their child smoking, by age

All pupils   *England 2000*

Attitude or expected attitude of family	Age					
	11 years	12 years	13 years	14 years	15 years	Total
	%	%	%	%	%	%
Non-smokers						
Family:						
Stop me	72	71	67	61	53	65
Persuade me not to	18	19	22	29	39	25
Don't mind	0	0	0	1	2	1
Encourage me	-	-	-	-	-	-
Not sure	10	10	10	9	6	9
Current smokers[a]						
Family:						
Stop me	43	48	35	31	25	31
Persuade me not to	36	25	43	49	53	47
Don't mind	-	6	5	7	12	8
Encourage me	-	2	0	1	0	1
Not sure	21	20	16	12	11	13
Bases						
Non-smokers	*1131*	*1333*	*1170*	*1070*	*1000*	*5704*
Current smokers	*53*	*101*	*257*	*369*	*558*	*1338*

[a] Among current smokers whose family do not know that they smoke, expected attitudes are shown.

Table 4.11

Family attitude to their child smoking, by age-standardised smoking behaviour

All pupils   *England 2000*

Attitude or expected attitude of family	Smoking status		
	Regular smokers[a]	Occasional smokers[a]	Non-smokers
	%	%	%
Stop me	27	45	64
Persuade me not to	49	35	26
Don't mind	10	3	1
Encourage me	2	1	-
Not sure	12	17	9
Bases	*732*	*606*	*5704*

[a] Among current smokers whose family do not know that they smoke, expected attitudes are shown.

5 Where children get cigarettes

Harriet Becher

5.1 Introduction

The Enforcement Protocol to tackle underage tobacco sales was launched on 13 September 2000 by representatives from the Department of Health, Local Authorities, Trading Standards Officers, and Environmental Health Officers. Local Authorities are to publish an annual review of enforcement action, as required by the Children and Young Person's (Protection from Tobacco) Act 1991. However, despite the fact that it is illegal to sell any tobacco product to children under the age of 16, previous surveys have shown that many children can and do buy cigarettes in shops and from vending machines.

Current smokers (both regular and occasional) were asked where they usually obtained their cigarettes. They were given the option to name more than one source, if they often got their cigarettes from different places or people. Current smokers were also asked how easy or difficult they found it to buy cigarettes from a shop.

In addition, the questionnaire asked all pupils (including non-smokers) whether they had tried to buy cigarettes from a shop in the past year. Those pupils who answered that they had tried to buy cigarettes from a shop were asked whether they had been refused. They were also asked whether their last attempt at purchase had been successful, and if so how many cigarettes they had bought that time. Finally, in order to measure frequency of purchase pupils were asked how often (if at all) they bought cigarettes from shops and vending machines.

5.2 Trends in how regular smokers obtain their cigarettes

The proportion of regular smokers buying cigarettes remained fairly constant – between 85% and 89% – from 1982 (when the question was first asked) to 1998. There was a small decrease from 1998 to 2000, so that the proportion of regular smokers buying cigarettes from shops was at its lowest at 80%, although it is not possible to tell whether this is the start of a decline in purchasing from shops. There has been a broad increase since 1982 in the proportion of regular smokers mentioning other sources of cigarettes. The questionnaire addresses source of cigarettes rather than volume, and it is possible that fewer cigarettes are obtained from these alternative sources. Nevertheless, the implication is that pupils are using a wider range of sources to obtain cigarettes than they were in 1982.

(Table 5.1, Figure 5.1)

5.3 Sources of cigarettes for regular and occasional smokers

Sources of cigarettes were very different for regular smokers when compared with occasional smokers. Regular smokers were more likely than occasional smokers to buy their cigarettes – all methods of buying cigarettes were more likely to be mentioned by regular smokers (for example 71% of regular smokers bought cigarettes from newsagents compared with 31% of occasional smokers). By far the most common method of getting cigarettes for occasional smokers was to be given them by their friends, mentioned by 74%, and this was the only method which was more common among occasional smokers than among regular smokers (it was mentioned by 50% of the latter group).

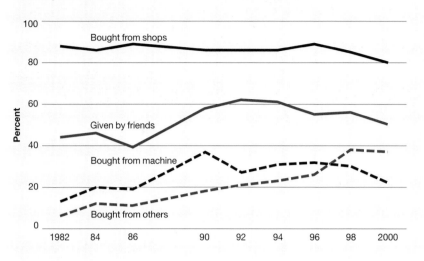

Figure 5.1

How smokers obtain their cigarettes: 1982-2000

Base: Regular smokers

The fact that regular smokers were more likely to buy cigarettes from shops may be partly because regular smokers tend to be older than occasional smokers, and therefore find it easier to buy cigarettes. This explanation might be supported by the fact that, as previous reports in this series have shown, older smokers are more likely to buy their cigarettes from shops than younger smokers. However, Table 5.4 suggests that the differences between regular and occasional smokers remain even after smoking status is age-standardised. It would seem that age per se is not a factor in the sources of cigarettes named by smokers. Rather, regular smokers are more likely than occasional smokers to buy their cigarettes, regardless of age. One explanation is that since regular smokers smoke more cigarettes per week than occasional smokers (as shown by this survey), they are more likely to need to buy cigarettes themselves rather than get them from friends. **(Tables 5.2-5.4)**

5.4 Perceived difficulty in buying cigarettes from a shop

Smokers were asked how difficult or easy they found it to purchase cigarettes from a shop, if they usually did so. Twenty one per cent of smokers in 2000 said that they found it difficult on the whole to buy cigarettes from a shop – meaning that for nearly four in five it was not perceived as difficult. A higher proportion of occasional smokers than regular smokers found it difficult (28% compared with 19%). These findings are very similar to those reported in 1998 and 1996. There was no significant difference between the proportions of boys and girls who said that they found it easy to buy cigarettes (this is in contrast to findings in 1998 and 1996, which suggested that boys were more likely than girls to say they found buying cigarettes difficult).

Perhaps unsurprisingly, a much higher proportion of those who had been refused cigarettes in the past year reported that it was difficult to buy cigarettes than those who had not been refused cigarettes – 23% compared with 5%. Nevertheless, three quarters (77%) of those who had been refused in the last year still said that on the whole it was easy to buy cigarettes from a shop, suggesting that children are not easily deterred by refusal. Again these patterns are similar to those reported in previous sweeps of the survey. **(Tables 5.5, 5.6)**

5.5 Cigarette purchase from shops in the last year

Since 1990 the proportion who report having tried to buy cigarettes from shops has fallen. In 2000, 19% of all pupils said they had tried to buy cigarettes in the past year. This is significantly lower than the 22% reported in 1998, and is the lowest level ever measured in this series of surveys.

Of those pupils who had tried to buy cigarettes in a shop, 45% had been refused at least once (9% of all pupils). This figure, the number of children refused as a proportion of those attempting to purchase cigarettes, has increased over time since 1986, when it was 31%.

Boys were slightly more likely than girls to have been refused at least once – this pattern has been shown in most previous surveys in the series. Younger children were more likely to have been refused cigarettes than older children; 63% of 12 year olds attempting to buy cigarettes had been refused at least once as opposed to 39% of 15 year olds.

(Tables 5.7, 5.8, Figures 5.2, 5.3)

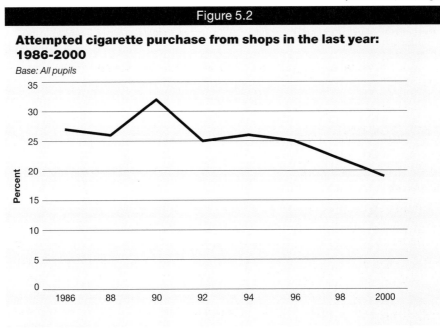

Figure 5.2

Attempted cigarette purchase from shops in the last year: 1986-2000

Base: All pupils

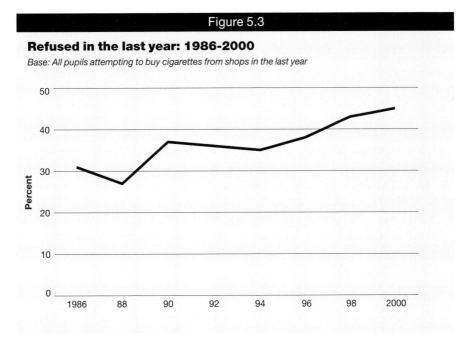

Figure 5.3

Refused in the last year: 1986-2000

Base: All pupils attempting to buy cigarettes from shops in the last year

5.6 Last time children tried to buy cigarettes from a shop

Those children who admitted having tried to buy cigarettes from a shop in the past year were asked about what had happened the last time they tried. In 2000, 15% of these pupils were refused at their last attempt. Unsurprisingly, success was strongly related to age; younger children were more likely than older children to have been refused the last time (47% of 11-12 year olds compared with 7% of 15 year olds). In each age group girls appeared a little less likely than boys to have been refused, although small numbers mean that this difference is only significant for 15 year olds. It is possible that this is because girls as young teenagers tend to mature slightly more quickly than boys, making it less obvious to shopkeepers that they may be under 16.

Regular smokers were also less likely to have been refused at their last attempt to buy cigarettes than occasional or non-smokers – 10% of regular smokers had been refused compared with 19% of occasional smokers and 19% of non-smokers. This difference reduces slightly when smoking status is age-standardised, suggesting that age does affect whether pupils were likely to be refused, but that their smoking status was a more important factor. This may be due to the fact that regular smokers are more likely to buy cigarettes from shops (as discussed in section 5.3), and are therefore more likely to know which shops will serve them. **(Tables 5.9-5.11)**

5.7 How many cigarettes were bought last time

Under the Children and Young Person's (Protection from Tobacco) Act 1991, it is an offence to sell cigarettes by retail to any person other than in pre-packed quantities of 10 or more cigarettes in their original package. Pupils who had been successful at their last attempt to purchase cigarettes were asked how many they had bought on that occasion.

Since 1988 the proportion of children buying packs of ten has increased, and the proportion of children buying packs of twenty has decreased. In 1988 38% of children had bought a pack of ten at their last purchase; this increased to 54% in 1998 and to 60% in 2000. One possibility is that the increasing cost of cigarettes may be deterring children from larger purchases. Four per cent of children in 2000 had bought less than 10 cigarettes at their last purchase. **(Tables 5.12-5.14)**

5.8 Frequency of purchase from shops and vending machines

All pupils were asked how often they bought cigarettes from shops and from vending machines. More than four in five pupils (81%) said that they never bought cigarettes from a shop, while 8% did so at least once a week. Seven per cent of pupils reported that they bought cigarettes from a machine. These figures are similar to those recorded in 1998, when these questions were first asked.

The guidelines produced and promoted by the National Association of Cigarette Machine Operators demand that machines be sited in areas where a nominated responsible adult can supervise them. Of those pupils who did use vending machines, 73% said that the last vending machine they had used was in a pub, club or restaurant where alcohol was for sale. Older children who used vending machines were more likely to use them in places where alcohol was for sale (83% of 15 year olds compared with 54% of 11-13 year olds had done so the last time). In addition, girls were more likely than boys to have used a vending machine in licensed premises. **(Tables 5.15-5.17)**

Table 5.1

Usual source of cigarettes for regular smokers: 1982 to 2000

Regular smokers   *England 1982-2000*

Usual source of cigarettes[a]	Year								
	1982	1984	1986	1990	1992	1994	1996	1998	2000
	%	%	%	%	%	%	%	%	%
Bought from shop[b]	88	86	89	86	86	86	89	85	80
Bought from machine	13	20	19	37	27	31	32	30	22
Bought from other people[c]	6	12	11	18	21	23	26	38	37
Given by friends	44	46	39	58	62	61	55	56	50
Given by brother/sister	9	7	12	19	16	18	16	20	12
Given by father/mother	10	7	7	5	7	7	7	11	6
Found or taken	1	1	2	3	4	6	6	6	6
Other	1	3	2	8	6	11	14	11	9
Bases	*325*	*474*	*300*	*305*	*310*	*348*	*360*	*496*	*719*

[a] Percentages total more than 100 because many pupils gave more than one answer.

[b] Up to 1986 (the question was not included in 1988) there was only one category for shop. This has been split into four since 1990, but for comparability, in this table all the shop categories have been collapsed into one code.

[c] Up to 1996 there was one category for bought from other people. This has been split into 'bought from friends/relatives' and 'bought from someone else' since 1998, to aid comparability, these categories have been collapsed into one code.

Table 5.2

Usual source of cigarettes for current smokers, by age

Current smokers   *England 2000*

Usual source of cigarettes[a]	Age				
	11-12 years	13 years	14 years	15 years	Total
	%	%	%	%	%
Bought from newsagents/tobacconist/sweet shop	18	36	57	72	57
Bought from garage shop	6	15	26	40	29
Bought from supermarket	2	6	11	25	16
Bought from other type of shop	4	7	7	15	10
Bought from machine	12	14	15	22	18
Bought from friends/relatives	27	27	20	20	22
Bought from someone else	27	22	17	12	16
Given by friends	68	62	63	53	59
Given by brother/sister	4	12	10	10	10
Given by father/mother	3	4	4	5	4
Found or taken	10	9	6	3	6
Other	20	15	8	5	9
Bases	*90*	*198*	*319*	*509*	*1116*

[a] Percentages total more than 100 because many pupils gave more than one answer.

Table 5.3

Usual source of cigarettes for current smokers, by smoking behaviour

Current smokers   *England 2000*

Usual source of cigarettes[a]	Smoking behaviour		
	Regular smokers	Occasional smokers	Total
	%	%	%
Bought from newsagents/ tobacconist/sweet shop	71	31	57
Bought from garage shop	39	11	29
Bought from supermarket	22	4	16
Bought from other type of shop	14	4	10
Bought from machine	22	10	18
Bought from friends/relatives	27	13	22
Bought from someone else	19	12	16
Given by friends	50	74	59
Given by brother/sister	12	5	10
Given by father/mother	6	1	4
Found or taken	6	5	6
Other	9	8	9
Bases	*719*	*397*	*1116*

[a] Percentages total more than 100 because many pupils gave more than one answer.

Table 5.4

Usual source of cigarettes for current smokers, by age-standardised smoking behaviour

Current smokers   *England 2000*

Usual source of cigarettes[a]	Smoking status	
	Regular smokers	Occasional smokers
	%	%
Bought from newsagents/ tobacconist/sweet shop	69	34
Bought from garage shop	37	12
Bought from supermarket	21	4
Bought from other type of shop	13	4
Bought from machine	22	11
Bought from friends/relatives	27	12
Bought from someone else	19	11
Given by friends	51	73
Given by brother/sister	12	5
Given by father/mother	6	1
Found or taken	6	5
Other	10	7
Bases	*719*	*397*

[a] Percentages total more than 100 because many pupils gave more than one answer.

Table 5.5

Perceived difficulty or ease of buying cigarettes from a shop, by sex and smoking status

Smokers who had bought from a shop   *England 2000*

Difficulty or ease of buying cigarettes	Sex		Smoking status		
	Boys	Girls	Regular smokers	Occasional smokers	Total
	%	%	%	%	%
Difficult	22	20	19	28	21
Easy	78	80	81	72	79
Bases	*380*	*508*	*650*	*238*	*888*

Table 5.6

Perceived difficulty or ease of buying cigarettes from a shop, by whether refused by a shopkeeper in the last year

Smokers who had bought from a shop   *England 2000*

Difficulty or ease of buying cigarettes	Refused by shopkeeper		Total
	Yes	No	
	%	%	%
Difficult	23	5	15
Easy	77	95	85
Bases	*391*	*347*	*738*

Table 5.7

Cigarette purchase from a shop in the last year, by sex: 1986 to 2000

All pupils   *England 1986-2000*

Cigarette purchase	Sex		
	Boys	Girls	Total
	%	%	%
% Who tried to buy cigarettes from a shop			
1986	25	30	27
1988	26	27	26
1990	30	33	32
1992	25	25	25
1994	24	29	26
1996	22	28	25
1998	20	23	22
2000	18	21	19
Was refused at least once in the last year:			
As % of those who tried to buy them			
1986	34	28	31
1988	30	26	27
1990	40	34	37
1992	36	36	36
1994	39	32	35
1996	36	39	38
1998	44	42	43
2000	47	44	45
As % of all pupils			
1986	8	9	8
1988	8	7	7
1990	12	11	12
1992	9	9	9
1994	9	9	9
1996	8	11	9
1998	8	10	9
2000	8	9	9
Bases			
Those who tried to buy cigarettes			
1986	409	454	865
1988	376	403	786
1990	488	483	971
1992	412	399	811
1994	364	434	798
1996	322	384	706
1998	442	539	981
2000	646	701	1347
All pupils			
1986	1757	1495	3157
1988	1469	1521	3016
1990	1627	1465	3092
1992	1657	1610	3267
1994	1516	1517	3033
1996	1443	1407	2850
1998	2330	2411	4741
2000	3604	3372	6976

Table 5.8

Cigarette purchase from a shop in the last year, by age: 1986 to 2000

All pupils   *England 1986-2000*

Cigarette purchase	Age					
	11 years	12 years	13 years	14 years	15 years	Total
	%	%	%	%	%	%
% Who tried to buy cigarettes from a shop						
1986	16	15	21	30	45	27
1988	10	13	21	31	46	26
1990	18	18	27	39	54	32
1992	9	11	17	35	50	25
1994	7	11	19	34	55	26
1996	5	10	19	34	54	25
1998	4	6	15	32	57	22
2000	3	6	12	27	43	19
Was refused at least once in the last year:						
As % of those who tried to buy them						
1986	41	47	39	30	22	31
1988	[47]	38	34	29	19	27
1990	46	52	44	31	29	36
1992	58	48	47	38	26	37
1994	[54]	42	38	42	27	35
1996	a	47	42	39	33	38
1998	a	53	51	46	36	43
2000	[50]	63	59	46	39	45
As % of all pupils						
1986	7	7	8	9	10	8
1988	5	5	7	9	9	7
1990	8	9	12	12	16	12
1992	5	6	8	13	13	9
1994	4	5	7	14	15	9
1996	3	5	8	13	18	9
1998	2	3	8	14	17	9
2000	2	4	7	12	17	9
Bases						
Those who tried to buy cigarettes						
1986	*74*	*96*	*128*	*198*	*369*	*865*
1988	*47*	*77*	*131*	*196*	*335*	*786*
1990	*105*	*110*	*158*	*234*	*360*	*971*
1992	*52*	*79*	*119*	*211*	*344*	*805*
1994	*35*	*67*	*123*	*207*	*366*	*798*
1996	*28*	*57*	*104*	*200*	*317*	*706*
1998	*22*	*42*	*102*	*401*	*661*	*982*
2000	*38*	*86*	*176*	*380*	*667*	*1347*
All pupils						
1986	*446*	*628*	*610*	*654*	*818*	*3157*
1988	*455*	*595*	*613*	*626*	*727*	*3016*
1990	*601*	*619*	*598*	*605*	*662*	*3092*
1992	*587*	*693*	*685*	*605*	*686*	*3256*
1994	*500*	*613*	*635*	*615*	*670*	*3033*
1996	*545*	*575*	*559*	*585*	*586*	*2850*
1998	*603*	*722*	*691*	*1276*	*1421*	*4742*
2000	*1162*	*1408*	*1422*	*1433*	*1551*	*6976*

a The sample base for these categories is too small for results to be shown.

Table 5.9

Last time tried to buy cigarettes from a shop, whether successful, by age

*All pupils who attempted to buy cigarettes from
a shop in the past year* *England 2000*

Whether successful last time	Age				
	11-12 years	13 years	14 years	15 years	Total
	Percentage successful last time				
Boys	53	65	84	91	81
Girls	54	78	86	96	87
Total	53	72	85	93	85
Bases					
Boys	*72*	*81*	*165*	*328*	*646*
Girls	*50*	*95*	*214*	*341*	*700*
Total	*122*	*176*	*379*	*669*	*1346*

Table 5.10

Last time tried to buy cigarettes from a shop, whether successful, by smoking status

*All pupils who attempted to buy cigarettes from
a shop in the past year* *England 2000*

Whether successful last time	Smoking status			
	Regular smokers	Occasional smokers	Non- smokers	Total
	%	%	%	%
Successful	90	81	81	85
Unsuccessful	10	19	19	15
Bases	*604*	*283*	*451*	*1338*

Table 5.11

Last time tried to buy cigarettes from a shop, whether successful, by age-standardised smoking status

*All pupils who attempted to buy cigarettes from
a shop in the past year* *England 2000*

Whether successful last time	Age-standardised smoking status			
	Regular smokers	Occasional smokers	Non- smokers	Total
	%	%	%	%
Successful	88	82	83	85
Unsuccessful	12	18	17	15
Bases	*604*	*283*	*451*	*1338*

Table 5.12

Last time cigarettes were bought, how many were bought: 1988 to 2000

All pupils who had successfully bought cigarettes from a shop at their last attempt   *England 1988-2000*

Cigarettes bought last time	Year						
	1988	1990	1992	1994	1996	1998	2000
	%	%	%	%	%	%	%
Fewer than 10[a]	2	2	1	2	2	3	4
Ten[b]	38	40	48	50	49	54	60
Twenty[c]	54	51	45	41	44	38	32
More than 20	6	7	6	7	5	6	3
Bases	693	809	680	686	614	821	1108

[a] Under the Children and Young Person's (Protection from Tobacco) Act 1991, it is an offence to sell cigarettes by retail to any person other than in pre-packed quantities of 10 or more cigarettes in their original package.

[b] This includes a few children who bought between 11 and 15 cigarettes.

[c] This includes a few children who bought between 16 and 19 cigarettes; this may include purchases of 'vending packs' (typically containing 16 or 17 cigarettes).

Table 5.13

Last time cigarettes were bought, how many were bought, by age

All pupils who had successfully bought cigarettes from a shop at their last attempt   *England 2000*

Cigarettes bought last time	Age				
	11-12 years	13 years	14 years	15 years	Total
	%	%	%	%	%
Fewer than 10 [a]	13	8	5	2	4
Ten[b]	62	57	59	62	60
Twenty[c]	20	31	33	33	32
More than 20	5	3	3	3	3
Bases	60	127	315	606	1108

[a] Under the Children and Young Person's (Protection from Tobacco) Act 1991, it is an offence to sell cigarettes by retail to any person other than in pre-packed quantities of 10 or more cigarettes in their original package.

[b] This includes a few children who bought between 11 and 15 cigarettes.

[c] This includes a few children who bought between 16 and 19 cigarettes; this may include purchases of 'vending packs' (typically containing 16 or 17 cigarettes).

Table 5.14

Last time cigarettes were bought, how many were bought, by smoking behaviour

All pupils who had successfully bought cigarettes from a shop at their last attempt   *England 2000*

Cigarettes bought last time	Smoking behaviour					
	Regular smoker	Occasional smoker	Used to smoke	Tried once	Never smoked	Total
	%	%	%	%	%	%
Fewer than 10[a]	1	4	7	7	15	4
Ten[b]	62	62	62	63	43	61
Twenty[c]	33	30	29	30	40	32
More than 20	4	3	2	1	2	3
Bases	535	223	140	121	86	1105

[a] Under the Children and Young Person's (Protection from Tobacco) Act 1991, it is an offence to sell cigarettes by retail to any person other than in pre-packed quantities of 10 or more cigarettes in their original package.

[b] This includes a few children who bought between 11 and 15 cigarettes.

[c] This includes a few children who bought between 16 and 19 cigarettes; this may include purchases of 'vending packs' (typically containing 16 or 17 cigarettes).

Table 5.15

How often pupils buy from shops and cigarette vending machines, by sex

All pupils   *England 2000*

How often buy	Purchase from shops			Purchase from machines		
	Boys	Girls	Total	Boys	Girls	Total
	%	%	%	%	%	%
Almost every day	3	3	3	0	0	0
Once or twice a week	4	5	5	1	1	1
Two or three times a month	2	3	2	1	1	1
About once a month	2	2	2	1	1	1
A few times a year	7	7	7	4	5	4
Never	83	80	81	94	92	93
Bases	*3577*	*3356*	*6933*	*3464*	*3250*	*6714*

Table 5.16

Last time used cigarette vending machine, where it was situated, by age

All pupils who have used a vending machine
to purchase cigarettes   *England 2000*

Where the machine was situated	Age			
	11-13 years	14 years	15 years	Total
	%	%	%	%
Pub/club/restaurant – alcohol for sale	54	75	83	73
Café/restaurant – alcohol not for sale	4	3	2	3
Arcade/bowling alley	19	9	5	10
Petrol station	6	2	1	2
Somewhere else	17	10	9	12
Bases	*120*	*116*	*224*	*460*

Table 5.17

Last time used cigarette vending machine, where it was situated, by sex

All pupils who have used a vending
machine to purchase cigarettes   *England 2000*

Where the machine was situated	Sex		
	Boys	Girls	Total
	%	%	
Pub/club/restaurant – alcohol for sale	66	79	73
Café/restaurant – alcohol not for sale	3	3	3
Arcade/bowling alley	13	8	10
Petrol station	3	2	2
Somewhere else	15	9	12
Bases	*202*	*258*	*460*

6 Drinking: Introduction

Jim Jamison, Ian Schagen and Peter Emery

6.1 Background

Although this series of surveys began in 1982, questions about alcoholic drinks did not feature in the questionnaire until 1990. The initial drinking content of the questionnaire consisted of a few questions about usual drinking behaviour, along with questions about the consumption of different types of drinks in the last seven days.

In 1996 the drinking section was expanded to ask more questions about general drinking behaviour and to add 'alcopops' (alcoholic lemonades, such as *Hooch*, and similar drinks) to the categories of drinks. In 2000, the definition of 'alcopops' was extended to include pre-mixed alcoholic drinks (such as *Bacardi Breezer*) and the examples given were updated.

One further question was added in 2000 on the specific days when alcohol had been drunk. However, since the 2000 survey questionnaire had to cover smoking, drinking and drug use and be completed within one school period, some of the general questions about drinking behaviour (such as where alcohol was usually drunk and who usually drank alcohol with) were omitted.

6.2 Self-reported alcohol consumption

The section on drinking begins by asking the pupils if they have 'ever had a proper alcoholic drink – a whole drink, not just a sip'. The section starts with this question so that those who have drunk alcohol are directed to more detailed questions while those who have not can be directed to the next section. In 2000, two fifths of the sample said that they had never had a proper alcoholic drink (a repeat of the 1998 and 1999 figures) and 3% said that they had done so but did not drink at all now, compared with 4% in both 1998 and 1999.

The range of alcoholic drinks available to young people continues to grow but it would be impractical to include every type of drink individually in this survey. Pupils who had drunk alcohol in the last seven days were asked how much they had drunk of different types of drink (not counting drinks labelled as low alcohol) and their answers were converted into units. Pupils were asked about the following types of drink:

- Beer, lager and cider
- Shandy
- Wine
- Martini and sherry
- Spirits and liqueurs
- 'Alcopops' and pre-mixed alcoholic drinks

A unit of alcohol is 8 grams by weight or 1cl (10ml) by volume of pure alcohol. This is the approximate amount contained in half a pint of ordinary strength beer or lager (4% alcohol by volume), a single pub measure of spirits (25ml), a small glass of ordinary strength wine (9% alcohol by volume), or a single pub measure of sherry or fortified wine. The following table shows how measures of each type of drink were converted into units of alcohol.

Type of drink	Measure	Units of alcohol
Beer, lager or cider	Pint	2
	Large can	1.5
	Half pint, small can or bottle	1
	Less than half a pint	0.5
Shandy	Pint	1
	Large can	0.75
	Half pint, small can or bottle	0.5
	Less than half a pint	0.25
Wine, fortified wine or spirits	Glass	1
	Less than a glass	0.5
Alcopops	Can or bottle	1
	Less than a bottle	0.5

In defining the number of units drunk, the alcoholic strength and volume measures of drinks are assumed to be the same – such that for example a pint of beer is defined as 2 units of alcohol regardless of the brand of beer, and a glass of wine is defined as 1 unit regardless of the size of the glass. It would be impractical to collect very accurate information on strength and volume in this type of survey. Hence, total alcohol consumption is estimated using a set of consistent assumptions, which nevertheless clearly imply a degree of approximation in these measurements.

Previous research[1] has found that if variation in alcoholic strength were taken into account, consumption of those aged 16-24 increased by about one fifth for young men and one tenth for young women. While that age group drinks more than those aged 11-15, the types of drink consumed may be similar and the alcohol consumption of those covered by this survey is likely to be underestimated for the same reason.

As discussed in Chapter 1, it may be reasonable to assume that young people are unlikely to deny the fact that they drink alcohol. There may, however, be some uncertainty about the accuracy of reported levels of consumption and under-reporting may be a real possibility. People responding to surveys may underestimate how much they drink, for a variety of reasons, including forgetfulness. Also, when developing the questionnaire, a balance had to be sought between the need to collect detailed information and the practicality of keeping the questionnaire straightforward so that pupils could complete it as reliably as possible.

Notes and references

1   Goddard E (1991) *Drinking in England and Wales in the late 1980s*. HMSO, London.

7 Drinking in the previous week

Jim Jamison, Ian Schagen and Peter Emery

7.1 Prevalence of drinking

Pupils who had ever drunk alcohol were asked if they had had an alcoholic drink in the last seven days. In 2000, 24% of the total sample of young people aged 11-15 in England said that they had. The proportion of pupils who had drunk in the last week has fluctuated between 20% and 27% since the question was first introduced in 1988, with no sustained increase or decrease over time.

In most previous surveys, boys have been more likely to have had a drink in the previous week than girls, although the gap between boys and girls has fluctuated over time. In 2000, there was no significant difference between the proportions of girls and boys who had drunk in the previous week. **(Table 7.1, Figures 7.1, 7.2)**

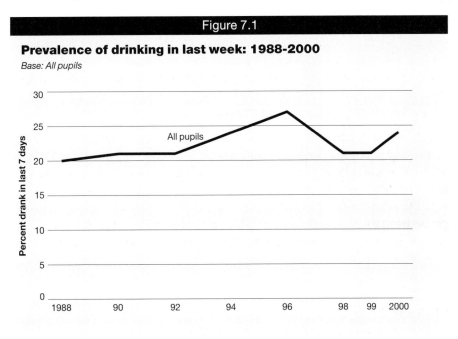

Figure 7.1

Prevalence of drinking in last week: 1988-2000
Base: All pupils

As in previous surveys, the proportions drinking in the last week increased sharply with age. Only 5% of those aged 11 had had a drink in the last week, but this increased greatly by age 14 and by age 15. One half (49%) of 15 year olds and a third (32%) of 14 year olds had drunk in the last week. Fifteen year old boys were more likely than 15 year old girls to have drunk in the last week (52% compared with 46%). **(Table 7.2, Figure 7.3)**

7.2 Drinking days in the last week

In 1998, those who drank in the last week were asked for the first time to indicate on which days in the last week they had had a drink. In 2000, 86% had drunk only on one or two days, while a very small proportion (3%) had done so on five or more days. Even among 15 year old drinkers, over 80% had drunk on no more than two days and usually only on one. As in 1998, weekends were the most popular times for drinking. Of those who had had a

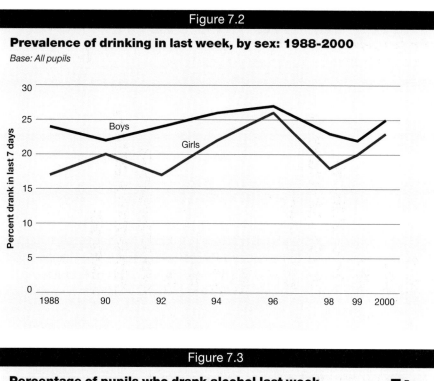

Figure 7.2

Prevalence of drinking in last week, by sex: 1988-2000

Base: All pupils

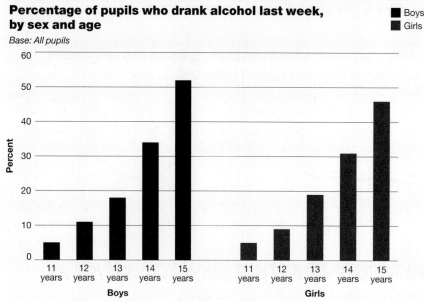

Figure 7.3

Percentage of pupils who drank alcohol last week, by sex and age

■ Boys
■ Girls

Base: All pupils

drink in the past seven days, 42% had done so on Friday, 54% on Saturday and 27% on Sunday. There was very little variation in the proportions of drinkers in each age group who drank on weekdays, but weekend drinking varies by age. The proportion of drinkers in the last week who drank on Friday increased with age, from 18% of pupils aged 11-12 to 50% of aged 15. There was a less marked but similar difference with Saturday drinking, with 46% of drinkers in the youngest age group drinking on a Saturday compared with 60% of the oldest age group.

(Tables 7.3-7.6, Figure 7.4)

7.3 **Alcohol consumption**

The rest of the analysis in this chapter mainly focuses on those who reported having drunk alcohol during the week before the survey – that is, 24% of the sample of 11-15 year olds. The information given is representative of what this age group drinks as a whole in a typical week, but is not a measure of what all pupils usually drink. This is because not all less frequent drinkers (who tend to be younger) would be asked the detailed questions about their drinking in the last week.

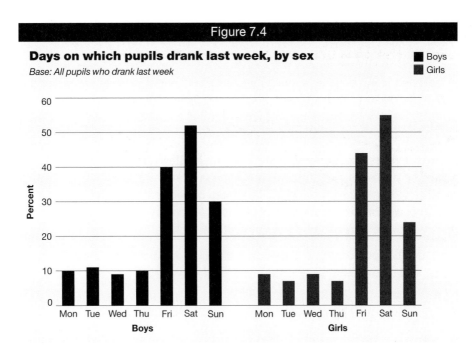

Figure 7.4

Days on which pupils drank last week, by sex
Base: All pupils who drank last week

■ Boys
■ Girls

Boys

Girls

7.4 Average weekly alcohol consumption per drinker

Pupils were asked how much alcohol they had drunk in the previous seven days. Although the proportion of pupils who drank in the previous week had fluctuated over time, there had been a clear increase in the amount of alcohol drunk by those who do drink. In 1990, pupils who drank consumed an estimated 5.3 units of alcohol in the past week, which had nearly doubled to 10.4 units in 2000. This magnitude of increase in the amount drunk by those who had drunk in the last seven days was found among both boys (5.7 units of alcohol in 1990, 11.6 in 2000) and girls (4.7 units in 1990, 9.1 in 2000).

Older pupils who drank, tended to drink more than their younger counterparts. Pupils aged 11-13 who drank in the last week averaged 6.4 units, while for 15 year old pupils' average consumption was twice this amount (12.8 units). The amount of alcohol drunk by those who had drunk in the previous week had nearly doubled between 1990 and 2000 for all age groups.   **(Tables 7.7-7.9, Figure 7.5)**

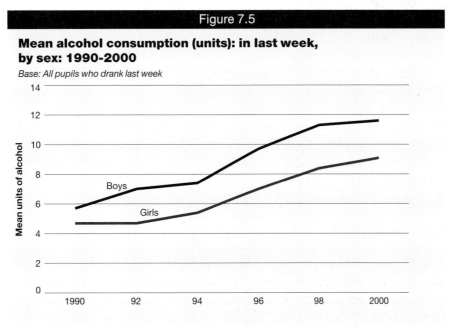

Figure 7.5

Mean alcohol consumption (units): in last week, by sex: 1990-2000
Base: All pupils who drank last week

Boys

Girls

7.5 Types of drink

As well as questions about beer, wine and spirits, the 2000 survey repeated questions included in 1996 and 1998 about 'alcopops' – alcoholic 'soft' drinks (such as Hooch) and pre-mixed alcoholic drinks (such as Bacardi Breezer and Smirnoff Ice) that were first available in 1995. The definition of 'alcopops' was extended for the 2000 survey to include examples of contemporary brands, particularly newly popular pre-mixed drinks.

Three quarters of drinkers, though somewhat more boys and fewer girls, had drunk beer, lager or cider in the last seven days. Around six in ten had drunk 'alcopops' and a similar proportion spirits, though these drinks were a little more popular among girls than boys. Wine drinking, too, was more common among girls (52%) than boys (38%). Drinking of shandy and fortified wine were each reported by a fifth of drinkers.

When we consider the consumption of types of alcohol by those drinking in the past week in the past ten years several features emerge:

- Among drinkers, prevalence of drinking beer, lager, cider, wine and fortified wine have all remained fairly steady over the period.

- Prevalence of drinking spirits has risen substantially from 35% of drinkers in 1990 to 59% in 2000.

- Among drinkers, prevalence of drinking shandy has decreased from 31% in 1990 to 20% in 2000.

In 1996 and 2000, around three fifths of pupils who had drunk in the last week reported drinking of 'alcopops'. In 1998, the equivalent proportion was around two fifths, which may have reflected the impact of changing fashions for these types of drink and, perhaps, non-inclusion of emerging new brands in the 1998 survey. It could also be explained due to the introduction of a voluntary code on the naming, packaging and merchandising of alcoholic drinks by the Portman Group (drinks industry body) in 1996, in response to criticism of the growing 'alcopop' market. This may have made certain 'alcopops' less appealing to children. In addition, the price of 'alcopops' was increased from January 1997 as a result of Budget measures, perhaps making them less affordable for many pupils.   **(Table 7.10)**

The types of drinks that pupils had drunk varied by age. Spirits and 'alcopops' were more likely to have been drunk by older pupils than younger ones, while the converse was the case for shandy and wine. There was no relationship between beer, lager or cider and age, nor was there for fortified wine.   **(Table 7.11)**

Pupils were also asked whether they usually drank normal strength or strong beer, lager or cider. Seventy per cent of those who had drunk alcohol in the past week indicated that they drank normal strength brands and 30% that they drank strong brands. The strength of beer normally drunk did not vary by age. Those who usually drank strong beer drank a greater amount of alcohol than those who usually drank normal strength beer, even without allowing for the extra alcohol in the higher strength brands - strong beer drinkers averaged 5.9 pints of beer in the last week compared with 3.6 pints for normal strength beer drinkers.   **(Table 7.12)**

7.6 Alcohol consumption of different types of drink

Overall levels of consumption among drinkers had increased from 5.3 units of alcohol in the last week in 1990 and 6.0 in 1992 to 10.4 in 2000. Consumption figures for individual drinks are not available for 1990, but it is possible to see changes in consumption of different types of drinks between 1992 and 2000. Although overall consumption has increased, there was no difference in the amount of shandy, wine or fortified wine drunk by pupils who drank in the previous week. Consumption of beer, lager or cider increased from 3.7 units in 1992 to 4.7 units in 2000, and drinking of spirits had more than doubled over time from 0.8 units in 1992 to 1.9 units in 2000. 'Alcopops' were first available in 1995 and consumption was first measured in 1996 at 1.4 units of alcohol among drinkers in the last week, and in 2000 the equivalent figure was 2.3 units. **(Table 7.13)**

Among pupils who drank, there was no difference between boys and girls in the amount of shandy, fortified wine, spirits or 'alcopops' drunk in the last week. However, boys drank more beer, lager or cider (6.3 units) than girls (2.9 units), whereas girls drank more wine – 1.4 units compared with 0.7 units among boys who drank. **(Table 7.14)**

In order to assess the impact of 'alcopops' it is necessary to look at trends in consumption of other drinks since alcopops were first introduced in 1996:

● The proportion drinking in the last week was lower in 2000 than in 1996.

● The proportion of those who drank in the last week who drank different types of drinks has remained stable between 1996 and 2000 for all types of drinks except spirits and fortified wines which have shown an increase.

● The amount of each type of drink drunk in the last week has remained stable, apart from spirits where the amount drunk has increased.

The introduction of alcopops to the market does not seem to have affected the number of pupils who drink but it has contributed to the increase in the total amount drunk by drinkers. Furthermore, it seems to be an extra type of drink that pupils can choose to drink, as its introduction has not resulted in a decrease in the amount of any other types of drink that were drunk. **(Table 7.14)**

An alternative way of looking at consumption is to look at the total consumption accounted for by different types of drink (for the purposes of this analysis shandy was included in with beer, lager and cider, and wine and fortified wine were combined). Among boys consumption is dominated by beer, lager, cider and shandy which account for 57% of alcohol units drunk by boys. Beers also accounted for more of the overall consumption for girls than other drinks, although not to the same extent as these drinks did for boys. A third (33%) of the alcohol drunk by girls in the last week was beer, lager or cider; 'alcopops' accounted for 26%, spirits 22% and wine and fortified wine 19%. **(Figure 7.6)**

Figure 7.6

Alcohol consumption of each type of drink as a percentage of the total, by sex

Base: All pupils who drank last week

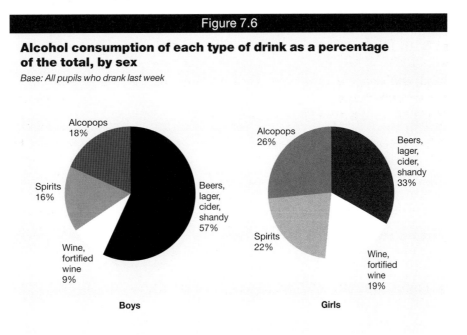

Boys

Girls

Table 7.1

When last had a drink, by sex: 1988 to 2000

All pupils   *England 1988-2000*

When last had a drink	Year							
	1988	1990	1992	1994	1996	1998	1999	2000
	%	%	%	%	%	%	%	%
Boys								
During the last week	24	22	24	26	27	23	22	25
One to four weeks ago	19	15	12	14	15	15	16	13
One to six months ago	12	13	13	11	12	12	12	11
More than six months ago	11	15	14	10	9	12	11	11
Never had a drink	35	35	37	39	37	38	38	39
Girls								
During the last week	17	20	17	22	26	18	20	23
One to four weeks ago	17	14	12	16	13	15	17	15
One to six months ago	13	13	14	12	13	13	12	11
More than six months ago	11	15	12	10	10	11	10	10
Never had a drink	41	38	44	40	38	42	41	40
Total								
During the last week	20	21	21	24	27	21	21	24
One to four weeks ago	18	15	12	15	14	15	16	14
One to six months ago	12	13	13	11	12	13	12	11
More than six months ago	11	15	13	10	9	11	11	10
Never had a drink	38	36	41	39	38	40	40	40
Bases								
Boys	*1427*	*1619*	*1646*	*1503*	*1432*	*2249*	*4816*	*3635*
Girls	*1518*	*1456*	*1606*	*1506*	*1391*	*2362*	*4558*	*3396*
Total	*3015*	*3082*	*3252*	*3009*	*2823*	*4609*	*9374*	*7031*

Table 7.2

Percentage who drank last week, by sex and age: 1988 to 2000

All pupils   *England 1988-2000*

Sex and age	Year								
	1988	1990	1992	1994	1996	1998	1999	2000	*2000 Bases*
	Pecentage who drank last week								
Boys									
11 years	7	8	8	8	7	4	7	5	*612*
12 years	12	9	13	10	12	14	10	11	*740*
13 years	20	17	15	22	27	16	16	18	*737*
14 years	25	32	32	34	37	28	28	34	*750*
15 years	45	42	49	52	50	48	48	52	*796*
Total	24	22	24	26	27	23	22	25	*3635*
Girls									
11 years	4	4	5	4	6	2	4	5	*564*
12 years	7	6	7	9	9	6	8	9	*681*
13 years	11	19	11	16	22	14	17	19	*696*
14 years	19	32	25	26	35	29	28	31	*691*
15 years	36	39	40	48	55	40	41	46	*764*
Total	17	20	17	22	26	18	20	23	*3396*
All pupils									
11 years	5	6	6	6	7	3	6	5	*1176*
12 years	9	8	10	9	11	10	9	10	*1421*
13 years	16	18	13	19	24	15	16	19	*1433*
14 years	22	32	29	30	36	29	28	32	*1441*
15 years	40	40	45	50	53	44	45	49	*1560*
Total	20	21	21	24	27	21	21	24	*7031*

Table 7.3

Number of drinking days in the last week, by sex: 1998, 2000

All pupils who drank last week *England 1998, 2000*

Number of drinking days	Survey year	
	1998	2000
	%	%
Boys		
1	57	68
2	21	17
3	10	8
4	6	3
5	2	2
6	1	1
7	3	1
Mean	1.9	1.6
Girls		
1	64	66
2	20	23
3	10	6
4	4	3
5	0	1
6	1	1
7	1	1
Mean	1.6	1.6
Total		
1	60	67
2	21	20
3	10	7
4	5	3
5	1	2
6	1	1
7	2	1
Mean	1.8	1.6
Bases		
Boys	*528*	*905*
Girls	*444*	*789*
Total	*968*	*1694*

Table 7.4

Number of drinking days in the last week, by age and sex

All pupils who drank last week *England 2000*

Number of drinking days	Age				
	11-12 years	13 years	14 years	15 years	Total
	%	%	%	%	%
Boys					
1	81	83	67	59	68
2	12	10	18	20	17
3	6	2	8	11	8
4	1	2	2	5	3
5	-	1	3	2	2
6	-	2	0	1	1
7	-	-	2	1	1
Mean	1.3	1.4	1.6	1.8	1.6
Girls					
1	87	73	70	55	66
2	11	18	20	29	23
3	1	5	7	7	6
4	-	3	3	4	3
5	-	1	-	2	1
6	-	-	0	1	1
7	1	-	-	1	1
Mean	1.2	1.4	1.5	1.8	1.6
Total					
1	84	78	68	58	67
2	12	14	19	24	20
3	4	4	7	9	7
4	1	3	3	5	3
5	-	1	2	2	2
6	-	1	0	1	1
7	1	-	1	1	1
Mean	1.2	1.4	1.6	1.8	1.6
Bases					
Boys	*110*	*133*	*254*	*408*	*905*
Girls	*90*	*135*	*212*	*352*	*789*
Total	*200*	*268*	*466*	*760*	*1694*

Table 7.5

Days on which children drank last week, by sex: 1998, 2000

All pupils who drank last week   *England 1998, 2000*

Drinking days	Survey year	
	1998	2000
	%	%
Boys		
Sunday	37	30
Monday	11	10
Tuesday	10	11
Wednesday	16	9
Thursday	11	10
Friday	43	40
Saturday	59	52
Girls		
Sunday	27	24
Monday	10	9
Tuesday	7	7
Wednesday	8	9
Thursday	8	7
Friday	45	44
Saturday	57	55
Total		
Sunday	33	27
Monday	10	10
Tuesday	9	9
Wednesday	12	9
Thursday	10	8
Friday	44	42
Saturday	58	54
Bases		
Boys	*526*	*905*
Girls	*442*	*789*
Total	*969*	*1694*

Table 7.6

Days on which children drank last week, by age and sex

All pupils who drank last week   *England 2000*

Drinking days	Age				
	11-12 years	13 years	14 years	15 years	Total
	%	%	%	%	%
Boys					
Sunday	31	30	30	29	30
Monday	5	11	11	11	10
Tuesday	12	10	11	10	11
Wednesday	5	8	10	11	9
Thursday	8	8	9	11	10
Friday	20	30	41	48	40
Saturday	45	38	53	59	52
Girls					
Sunday	26	26	25	23	24
Monday	10	4	8	11	9
Tuesday	8	7	6	9	7
Wednesday	10	8	7	11	9
Thursday	4	4	4	10	7
Friday	16	37	46	53	44
Saturday	47	54	50	61	55
Total					
Sunday	29	28	27	26	27
Monday	8	8	10	11	10
Tuesday	10	8	9	9	9
Wednesday	8	8	9	11	9
Thursday	7	6	6	11	8
Friday	18	34	43	50	42
Saturday	46	46	52	60	54
Bases					
Boys	*110*	*133*	*254*	*408*	*905*
Girls	*90*	*135*	*212*	*352*	*789*
Total	*200*	*268*	*466*	*760*	*1694*

Table 7.7

Mean alcohol consumption of those who had drunk in the last seven days, by sex and age: 1990 to 2000

All pupils who drank last week *England 1990-2000*

Sex and age	Year						
	1990	1992	1994	1996	1998	2000	*2000 Bases*
	Mean number of units						
Boys							
11-13 years	a	3.6	5.2	7.1	6.2	8.4	*163*
14 years	a	5.3	6.7	7.3	12.3	9.5	*205*
15 years	a	9.6	8.8	12.9	12.9	14.4	*351*
Total	5.7	7.0	7.4	9.7	11.3	11.6	*719*
Girls							
11-13 years	a	3.1	3.0	4.0	6.4	4.6	*184*
14 years	a	3.8	5.5	8.2	8.1	10.0	*187*
15 years	a	6.0	6.6	8.0	9.7	11.2	*321*
Total	4.7	4.7	5.4	7.0	8.4	9.1	*692*
All pupils							
11-13 years	a	3.4	4.1	5.5	6.3	6.4	*347*
14 years	a	4.7	6.1	7.7	9.9	9.7	*392*
15 years	a	8.1	7.7	10.4	11.5	12.8	*672*
Total years	5.3	6.0	6.4	8.4	9.9	10.4	*1411*

a Figures are not available by age group for 1990 data.

Table 7.8

Mean units of alcohol consumed in last seven days, by sex: 1990 to 2000

All pupils *England 1990-2000*

Alcohol consumption (units)	Year					
	1990	1992	1994	1996	1998	2000
	%	%	%	%	%	%
Boys	0.9	1.4	1.5	2.1	1.9	2.4
Girls	0.7	0.7	1.0	1.5	1.2	1.9
Total	0.8	1.1	1.3	1.8	1.6	2.2
Bases						
Boys	*1499*	*1581*	*1429*	*1346*	*2093*	*3440*
Girls	*1358*	*1561*	*1460*	*1330*	*2273*	*3298*
Total	*2857*	*3142*	*2889*	*2676*	*4367*	*6738*

Table 7.9

Alcohol consumption in the last seven days, by sex

All pupils who drank last week *England 2000*

Alcohol consumption (units)	Sex		
	Boys	Girls	Total
	%	%	%
Less than 1 unit over the week	6	8	7
1-6 units	44	48	46
7-13 units	23	25	24
14 units or more	28	20	24
Mean number of units	11.6	9.1	10.4
Median number of units	7.0	5.5	6.0
Bases	*719*	*692*	*1411*

Table 7.10

Types of alcohol in drunk in the last seven days, by sex: 1990 to 2000

All pupils who drank last week   *England 1990-2000*

Types of drink	Year					
	1990	1992	1994	1996	1998	2000
	%	%	%	%	%	%
Boys						
Beer, lager, cider	76	81	82	81	78	85
Shandy	38	26	27	22	19	23
Wine	44	46	44	38	47	38
Fortified wine	14	15	12	11	16	17
Spirits	33	38	37	42	52	55
Alcopops	a	a	a	52	33	55
Girls						
Beer, lager, cider	56	67	70	67	63	63
Shandy	22	23	21	18	18	15
Wine	56	60	52	43	55	52
Fortified wine	22	20	18	19	24	21
Spirits	38	36	42	48	56	63
Alcopops	a	a	a	58	42	69
Total						
Beer, lager, cider	67	76	76	74	71	75
Shandy	31	25	24	20	18	20
Wine	50	52	48	40	51	44
Fortified wine	18	17	15	15	20	19
Spirits	35	37	39	45	54	59
Alcopops	a	a	a	55	37	62
Bases						
Boys	*339*	*394*	*375*	*372*	*446*	*914*
Girls	*284*	*275*	*324*	*349*	*410*	*790*
Total	*623*	*669*	*699*	*721*	*856*	*1704*

a   Alcopops were first introduced in the 1996 survey.

Table 7.11

Types of alcohol drunk in the last seven days, by age

All pupils who drank last week   *England 2000*

Type of drink	Age				
	11-12 years	13 years	14 years	15 years	Total
	%	%	%	%	%
Beer, lager, cider	70	71	77	76	75
Shandy	36	29	18	13	20
Wine	56	51	46	39	44
Fortified wine	21	19	20	17	19
Spirits	40	54	65	62	59
Alcopops	48	63	63	64	62
Bases	*205*	*269*	*468*	*762*	*1704*

Table 7.12

Whether usually drinks strong or normal strength beers, by sex and age

All pupils who drank, beer, lager or cider last week *England 2000*

Type of beer, lager or cider last week	Age			
	11-13 years	14 years	15 years	Total
	%	%	%	%
Boys				
Normal strength beer	76	68	73	72
Strong beer	24	32	27	28
Girls				
Normal strength beer	68	65	69	67
Strong beer	32	35	31	33
Total				
Normal strength beer	73	67	71	70
Strong beer	27	33	29	30
Bases				
Boys	*128*	*171*	*326*	*625*
Girls	*74*	*102*	*169*	*345*
Total	*202*	*273*	*495*	*970*

Table 7.13

Alcohol consumption (units) of different types of drink: 1992 to 2000

All pupils who drank last week *England 1992-2000*

Type of drink	Year				
	1992	1994	1996	1998	2000
	Mean number of units				
Beer, lager, cider	3.7	4.0	4.7	5.7	4.7
Shandy	0.2	0.2	0.2	0.3	0.2
Wine	1.0	0.9	0.7	1.2	1.0
Fortified wine	0.3	0.2	0.2	0.4	0.3
Spirits	0.8	1.0	1.2	1.4	1.9
Alcopops	a	a	1.4	1.0	2.3
Total	6.0	6.4	8.4	9.9	10.4
Bases	*544*	*569*	*585*	*686*	*1411*

Table 7.14

Alcohol consumption (units) of different types of drink, by sex

All pupils who drank last week *England 2000*

Types of drink (mean units)	Sex		
	Boys	Girls	Total
Beer, lager, cider	6.3	2.9	4.7
Shandy	0.2	0.2	0.2
Wine	0.7	1.4	1.0
Fortified wine	0.3	0.3	0.3
Spirits	1.8	2.0	1.9
Alcopops	2.1	2.4	2.3
Total	11.6	9.1	10.4
Bases	*719*	*692*	*1411*

a Alcopops were first introduced in the 1996 survey.

8 Usual drinking behaviour

Jim Jamison and Ian Schagen

8.1 Introduction

All of the pupils who said that they had ever had a proper alcoholic drink were asked how often they usually drank alcohol, when they last drank alcohol, and from where they usually buy their alcohol. It should be borne in mind that some children in this age group will not have regular settled patterns of behaviour and some may have found the questions difficult to answer.

8.2 Usual drinking frequency

As reported in Chapter 7, two fifths of the whole sample had never had a 'proper alcoholic drink', but this is strongly related to age. Seventy six per cent of 11 year olds reported that they had never had an alcoholic drink, but this fell to just 14% among the 15 year old pupils.

Just under a fifth (18%) of 11-15 year olds said that they usually had an alcoholic drink at least weekly. In 1999, a similar proportion (17%) claimed to drink every week. This proportion appears to have remained fairly stable in recent years, as in 1998 the figure was 16% and in 1996 it was 20%. Of course many more 15 year olds – four in ten – drink weekly, including a small but significant proportion (5%) of 15 year old boys who claim to drink almost every day.[1]

The proportion of boys reporting that they drink at least weekly has been consistently higher than that of girls. In 2000 this difference remained, with 19% of boys and 17% of girls usually having an alcoholic drink at least once a week.   **(Tables 8.1, 8.2)**

8.3 Buying alcohol

Pupils who had ever had an alcoholic drink were asked to indicate where they usually bought alcohol and were given a list of five named sources to tick, a sixth category 'from someone else' and a final category of 'I never buy alcohol'. Just under half (46%) ticked this final category. This repeats the finding from the 1996, 1998 and 1999 surveys that one in two of the pupils who had ever had a drink had never actually bought alcohol.

Those who did buy alcohol most commonly did so from friends or relatives (17%) and off-licences (17%). In recent years, there appears to have been a notable shift towards buying from friends and relatives and away from purchasing in off-licences. However, it is not possible to tell whether alcohol purchased by friends or relatives was done so legitimately (by an older relative or friend to bypass the underage sales legislation), or whether the alcohol was smuggled illegally. Prevalence of purchasing from an off-licence fell from 27% in 1996 to 17% in 2000, in contrast purchasing from friends or relatives increased from 9% in 1998 to 17% in 2000. Purchasing of alcohol from shops or supermarkets over this period has also declined: 13% having been reported in 1996, 10% in 1998, 12% in 1999, with a decline to 9% in 2000. Reported purchases from a pub or bar (9%), from a club or disco (7%) and from 'somewhere else' (8%) have remained fairly consistent over the past four surveys.

The 2000 survey confirms that a minority of 11 and 12 year olds are able to buy alcohol at shops and licenced premises. The numbers doing so expand rapidly in the early teenage years. By the age of 15, three pupils in ten were buying alcohol from off-licences and two in 10 were being served in pubs or bars. **(Tables 8.3, 8.4, Figure 8.1)**

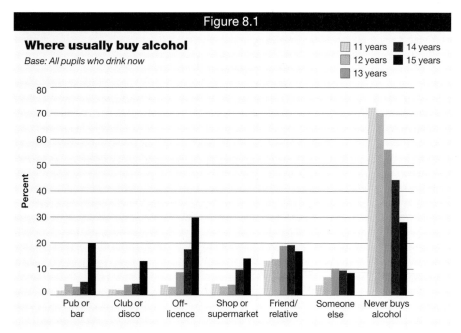

Figure 8.1

Where usually buy alcohol
Base: All pupils who drink now

11 years, 12 years, 13 years, 14 years, 15 years

As in previous years, the less frequent drinkers were more likely than the more frequent drinkers to report that they never bought alcohol. Forty one per cent of 15 year olds who drank less than once a week never bought alcohol compared with only 13% of those who drank at least once a week. Purchasing from official outlets was higher among frequent drinkers than among less frequent, but there was no difference in the proportions of frequent versus less frequent drinkers who bought alcohol from friends or relatives or from someone else. **(Table 8.5)**

Notes and references

1 In the 2000 survey, 8% reported that they usually had a drink about once a fortnight and 9% indicated once a month. If the fortnightly figure is halved and the monthly divided by four and then these figures are added to the 18% who usually drink each week, this produces an estimate of 24% for the percentage expected to be have an alcoholic drink in any given week. This figure matches the 24% who said that they had a drink during the week prior to the survey (see previous Chapter), underlining that in any one week about a quarter of 11-15 year olds drink alcohol.

Table 8.1

Usual drinking frequency, by sex and age

All pupils   _England 2000_

Usual drinking frequency	Age					
	11 years	12 years	13 years	14 years	15 years	Total
	%	%	%	%	%	%
Boys						
Almost every day	0	0	1	2	5	2
About twice a week	2	2	5	12	19	9
About once a week	1	3	8	12	19	9
At least once a week	_4_	_6_	_15_	_26_	_43_	_19_
About once a fortnight	1	3	7	12	14	8
About once a month	2	6	11	11	12	9
Only a few times a year	15	24	27	26	15	21
I never drink alcohol now	4	4	4	3	2	3
Never had a drink	74	57	37	23	14	39
Girls						
Almost every day	0	0	1	0	1	1
About twice a week	2	2	4	8	19	7
About once a week	1	2	8	13	18	9
At least once a week	_2_	_4_	_13_	_22_	_38_	_17_
About once a fortnight	2	3	7	12	17	9
About once a month	2	7	11	13	13	9
Only a few times year	13	22	27	27	17	21
I never drink alcohol now	3	5	5	3	2	4
Never had a drink	78	59	38	23	14	40
Total						
Almost every day	0	0	1	1	3	1
About twice a week	2	2	5	10	19	8
About once a week	1	3	8	13	18	9
At least once a week	_3_	_5_	_14_	_24_	_40_	_18_
About once a fortnight	2	3	7	12	15	8
About once a month	2	7	11	12	12	9
Only a few times a year	14	23	27	26	16	21
I never drink alcohol now	3	5	4	3	2	3
Never had a drink	76	58	37	23	14	40
Bases						
Boys	_614_	_745_	_738_	_748_	_795_	_3640_
Girls	_567_	_681_	_694_	_689_	_763_	_3394_
Total	_1181_	_1426_	_1432_	_1437_	_1558_	_7034_

Table 8.2

Usual drinking frequency, by sex: 1996 to 2000

All pupils   *England 1996-2000*

Usual drinking frequency	Year			
	1996	1998	1999	2000
	%	%	%	%
Boys				
Almost every day	2	2	2	2
About twice a week	8	8	7	9
About once a week	12	8	10	9
At least once a week	*21*	*18*	*19*	*19*
About once a fortnight	8	8	8	8
About once a month	8	8	8	9
Only a few times a year	22	24	23	21
Never drinks now	4	5	4	3
Never had a drink	37	38	38	39
Girls				
Almost every day	2	1	1	1
About twice a week	7	6	6	7
About once a week	10	8	9	9
At least once a week	*18*	*14*	*15*	*17*
About once a fortnight	10	7	9	9
About once a month	9	9	9	9
Only a few times a year	21	23	22	21
Never drinks now	3	4	3	4
Never had a drink	39	42	41	40
Total				
Almost every day	2	2	1	1
About twice a week	7	7	7	8
About once a week	11	8	9	9
At least once a week	*20*	*16*	*17*	*18*
About once a fortnight	9	7	9	8
About once a month	9	9	8	9
Only a few times a year	21	23	23	21
Never drinks now	4	4	4	3
Never had a drink	38	40	39	40
Bases				
Boys	*1431*	*2245*	*4823*	*3640*
Girls	*1387*	*2356*	*4568*	*3394*
Total	*2818*	*4607*	*9391*	*7034*

Table 8.3

Where children usually buy alcohol, by sex and age

All pupils who drink now   *England 2000*

Where usually buys alcohol[a]	Age					
	11 years	12 years	13 years	14 years	15 years	Total
	%	%	%	%	%	%
Boys						
In a pub or bar	2	4	4	4	20	9
In a club or disco	1	1	2	3	9	5
From an off-licence	5	2	9	17	31	17
From a shop or supermarket	5	3	3	9	14	8
From a friend or relative	14	9	18	18	16	16
From someone else	4	10	10	11	7	9
I never buy alcohol	71	71	58	46	29	48
Girls						
In a pub or bar	3	4	3	6	21	10
In a club or disco	4	2	6	5	16	9
From an off-licence	2	4	9	19	29	17
From a shop or supermarket	3	3	4	11	14	9
From a friend or relative	12	19	20	21	19	19
From someone else	4	3	10	7	8	7
I never buy alcohol	73	68	54	42	26	44
Total						
In a pub or bar	2	4	3	5	20	9
In a club or disco	2	2	4	4	13	7
From an off-licence	4	3	9	18	30	17
From a shop or supermarket	4	3	4	10	14	9
From a friend or relative	13	14	19	19	17	17
From someone else	4	7	10	9	8	8
I never buy alcohol	72	70	56	44	28	46
Bases						
Boys	*132*	*289*	*434*	*555*	*660*	*2070*
Girls	*104*	*238*	*392*	*507*	*641*	*1882*
Total	*236*	*527*	*826*	*1062*	*1301*	*3952*

[a] Percentages total more than 100, because pupils could give more than one answer.

Table 8.4

Where children usually buy alcohol, by sex: 1996 to 2000

All pupils who drink now   *England 1996-2000*

Where usually buy alcohol[a]	Year			
	1996	1998	1999	2000
	%	%	%	%
Boys				
In a pub or bar	8	9	8	9
In a club or disco	4	6	4	5
From an off-licence	26	22	22	17
From a shop or supermarket	12	11	11	8
From a friend/relative	b	10	9	16
From somewhere else	10	7	8	9
I never buy alcohol	51	51	5	48
Girls				
In a pub or bar	12	9	10	10
In a club or disco	8	6	7	9
From an off-licence	28	18	21	17
From a shop or supermarket	14	10	12	9
From a friend/relative	b	9	9	19
From somewhere else	6	6	7	7
I never buy alcohol	47	56	47	44
Total				
In a pub or bar	10	9	9	9
In a club or disco	6	6	5	7
From an off-licence	27	20	21	17
From a shop or supermarket	13	10	12	9
From a friend/relative	b	9	9	17
From somewhere else	8	6	8	8
I never buy alcohol	49	53	49	46
Bases				
Boys	*838*	*1427*	*2772*	*2070*
Girls	*802*	*1400*	*2527*	*1882*
Total	*1640*	*2827*	*5299*	*3952*

[a] Percentages total more than 100, because pupils could give more than one answer.

[b] Friends/relatives was introduced as a separate answer category in 1998.

Table 8.5

Where children usually buy alcohol, by age and usual drinking frequency

All pupils who drink now   *England 2000*

Where usually buys alcohol[a]	Age				
	11-12 years	13 years	14 years	15 years	Total
	%	%	%	%	%
Usually drinks at least once a week					
In a pub or bar	8	6	7	30	18
In a club or disco	5	6	6	20	13
From an off-licence	12	21	31	42	33
From a shop or supermarket	8	9	15	17	14
From a friend or relative	22	27	18	15	19
From someone else	17	13	14	7	11
I never buy alcohol	41	30	24	13	21
Usually drinks less than once a week					
In a pub or bar	3	2	4	11	5
In a club or disco	1	3	3	7	4
From an off-licence	2	5	11	18	9
From a shop or supermarket	3	2	7	11	6
From a friend or relative	12	16	20	19	17
From someone else	4	9	7	9	7
I never buy alcohol	75	64	54	41	58
Bases					
Drinks at least once a week	*103*	*198*	*343*	*628*	*1272*
Drinks less than once a week	*660*	*628*	*719*	*678*	*2680*

[a] Percentages total more than 100, because pupils could give more than one answer.

9 Drug use: Introduction

Jim Jamison and Ian Schagen

9.1 The Policy Context

The government published a ten-year strategy to tackle drug use in 1998,[1] which included the following Key Performance Targets:

> *'To reduce the proportion of people under the age of 25 reporting the use of Class A drugs by 25 per cent by 2005 (and by 50 per cent by 2008).'*

> *'To reduce the availability of Class A drugs by 25 per cent by 2005 (and by 50 per cent by 2008).'*

This survey measures the proportion of children aged 11-15 who have been offered drugs and who have used drugs, and thus contributes to the monitoring of these targets.

9.2 Obtaining information about drug use

This survey first gathered national information on drug use among young teenagers in 1998. The 1999 survey provided more detailed information on drug use, as well as children's experience and awareness of drug issues (although some limited information on solvent abuse was provided by the 1994 survey).

The questions on drugs continue to be developed from year to year. The main changes to the questions are not so extensive as to preclude comparisons with previous surveys. However, tables comparing drug use in 2000 with drug use in previous years should be read with more caution than is necessary for similar tables of smoking and drinking data.[2]

9.3 Groupings of drugs in analysis

Some tables provide data on pupils' knowledge or experience involving specific drugs. Within these tables, certain sets of drugs which have a similar chemical effect can logically be grouped together. The groupings used are as follows:

- Stimulants: cocaine, crack, ecstasy, amphetamines, poppers
- Psychedelics: LSD, magic mushrooms
- Opiates: heroin, methadone

9.4 Definition of Class A drugs

Table 9.1 lists the specific drugs that pupils were asked about in this survey, and indicates their classification under the Misuse of Drugs Act. This divides controlled drugs into three categories according to their harmfulness: Class A drugs are considered to cause the most harm. **(Table 9.1)**

This report includes prevalence of use of Class A drugs, although the following points need to be borne in mind about the definition of use of Class A drugs:

- The classification of certain drugs depends on the method of delivery used. For example, amphetamines are a Class B drug if taken orally and a Class A drug if injected. Therefore, we cannot state whether the amphetamine use reported in the survey should be reported as 'Class A' or 'Class B'.

- The Class A drugs mentioned in the survey (amphetamines when injected, ecstasy, cocaine, crack, heroin, LSD, magic mushrooms, methadone) are not an exhaustive list of Class A drugs.

Notes and references

1 *Tackling drugs to build a better Britain*, Cm 3945, The Stationery Office (1998).

2 In all three years of the survey, pupils have been asked to indicate on a list of drugs which, if any, they had heard of and which had been offered to them. In light of responses in 1998, the question structure was changed. In 1998 pupils had been asked to tick next to any and all the drugs that applied, whereas in 1999 (and 2000) they were asked to tick 'yes' or 'no' separately for each drug on the list. This change was designed to reduce the level of item non-response, since pupils would be less likely to overlook any drug if they had to go through the list systematically.

Pupils were also asked whether they had taken any of the drugs on the list, and if so, when was the last time they took each drug. To improve the accuracy of pupils' responses, the street names of each of the drugs were also included. To give some idea as to whether children were over-reporting their awareness of and use of drugs, a bogus substance called 'Semeron' was included in the list. In 1998, Semeron was also described as 'Bang' which is sometimes used as a street name for cannabis, and thus there was some confusion as to the true level of over-reporting in that year, although less than 0.5% use of Semeron was reported in 1998 and 1999 (Bang was removed from the list of street names for Semeron from 1999). Over-reporting of the use of cocaine is also possible in all years, since the street name for cocaine, 'Coke' may have been recognised by children (particularly the younger ones), who were actually thinking of cola drinks. Other amendments to street names have also been made since 1998 to reflect changes in the drug market.

When drawing comparisons over time, it is important to note two further changes to the survey. In 1998 one of the categories of drugs was 'Glue or Solvents', in 1999 an additional category of 'Gas (Butane, lighter refills)' was added, and then in 2000 the two categories were combined to become 'Gas, Aerosols, Glue and other solvents'.

In all years, pupils were given the opportunity to report having heard of, been offered or used 'other drugs' that were not named on the list. In 1998, details of these drugs were not obtained, so it was impossible to know whether pupils actually had an illegal drug in mind. In 1999 and 2000, pupils were asked to write in the names of these other drugs and sometimes these answers could be transferred back to an appropriate named drug on the list. Other drugs that were not relevant, such as prescription drugs or paracetemol could also be excluded. This change may explain why in 2000, there is less reporting of the use of 'other drugs' than in 1998.

Table 9.1		

Drug classifications under Misuse of Drugs Act 1971

Drug	Mode of use	Classification
Amphetamines	Inject	A
Ecstasy	Oral	A
Cocaine	Sniff or inject	A
Crack	Inject or smoke	A
Heroin	Smoke, sniff or inject	A
LSD	Oral	A
Magic Mushrooms	Oral	A
Methadone	Oral	A
Amphetamines	Sniff or oral	B
Cannabis	Smoke or oral	B
Tranquillisers	Oral or inject	B/C (depends on drug)
Anabolic steroids	Oral or inject	C
Poppers	Sniff	It is an offence to supply these
Glue	Sniff	substances if it is likely that the
Gas	Sniff	product is intended for abuse

10 Drug use

Jim Jamison, Ian Schagen and Peter Emery

10.1 Awareness of different drugs

In 2000, pupils had high levels of awareness of many drugs, though these levels were slightly below those found in 1999. In 2000, 8% reported that they had never heard of any of the drugs listed compared with just 4% in 1999.

On individual drugs cannabis (88%), cocaine (86%) and heroin (85%) had been heard of by very high proportions of pupils. Crack (76%) and ecstasy (70%) had been heard of by at least seven out of ten pupils, while awareness was a little lower for amphetamines (64%), magic mushrooms (64%), and LSD (59%). Poppers, methadone and anabolic steroids were the only drugs of which most pupils were unaware.

Awareness levels were very similar among boys and girls, although boys were more likely than girls to have heard of anabolic steroids, which may be due to the use of anabolic steroids in bodybuilding. **(Table 10.1)**

Awareness of every type of drug increases with age. Yet even at age 11 there were high levels of awareness of cannabis (76%), cocaine (76%) and heroin (74%). There was much less awareness of ecstasy and amphetamines at this age, but with age more and more pupils had heard of these drugs. Indeed, by the age of 15 over 80% of pupils were aware of each of a wide range of drugs: cannabis, cocaine, crack, ecstasy, amphetamines, LSD, magic mushrooms and heroin. **(Table 10.2)**

10.2 The types of drugs pupils have been offered

In both 1999 and 2000, just over a third of the pupils surveyed had been offered at least one of the listed drugs. Cannabis (28%) had been offered to substantially more pupils than any other drug. Indeed, apart from gas, aerosols, glue and other solvents (13%), no other drug had been offered to more than 8% of pupils. However, at least one pupil in six had been offered a drug in the 'stimulants' category. Boys were marginally more likely to be offered drugs than girls (38% and 34% respectively), which was a pattern that had also been seen in 1998 and 1999.

Older children were much more likely to have been offered drugs than younger children. Over half of 15 year olds (56%) had been offered cannabis compared to 6% of 11 year olds, and one third (32%) had been offered at least one stimulant, compared to 7% of 11 year olds. **(Tables 10.3, 10.4)**

10.3 Prevalence of drug use

In 2000, around one pupil in six (16%) reported that they had ever used one or more drugs, 14% had used drugs in the past year and 9% had taken drugs in the last month. The 2000 figures for drug use were marginally above those recorded in the previous two years – use of drugs in the last month had increased from 7% in 1998 to 9% in 2000, and use of drugs in the last year increased from 11% to 14% over the same period. All three surveys have shown the rate of drug use among boys to be a couple of percentage points above that among girls.[1] **(Table 10.5, Figure 10.1)**

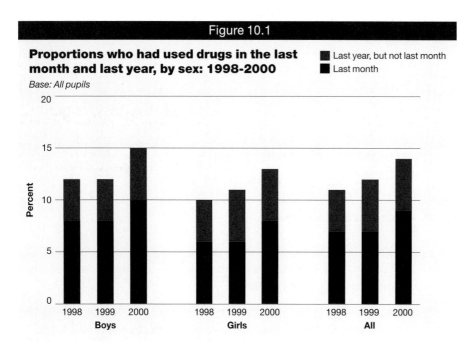

Figure 10.1

Proportions who had used drugs in the last month and last year, by sex: 1998-2000

■ Last year, but not last month
■ Last month

Base: All pupils

There was a steep increase with age in the proportions of young people who had taken drugs in the last month and in the last year. Three per cent of 11 year olds had taken drugs in the last month compared with 21% of 15 year olds, and the age gradient was even steeper for the use of drugs in the last year – 3% of 11 year olds compared with 29% of 15 year olds. **(Table 10.5, Figure 10.2)**

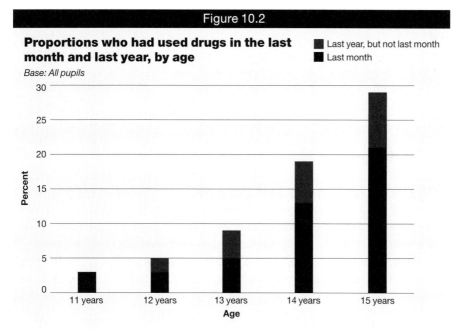

Figure 10.2

Proportions who had used drugs in the last month and last year, by age

■ Last year, but not last month
■ Last month

Base: All pupils

10.4 Types of drug used in the last year

Cannabis was by far the most widely used drug. Twelve per cent reported use of this drug in the last year (compared with 14% reporting the use of any drug in the last year). Every other individual drug had been used by no more than 3% in the last year, with a total of 4% using any Class A drug.

However, by age 15 29% had used at least one drug in the last twelve months, nearly all of whom had used cannabis (compared to 3% of 11 year olds reporting the use of any drug in the last year). Nine per cent of 15 year olds had used at least one Class A drug, though use

Smoking, drinking and drug use among young people in England in 2000

of cocaine and heroin was 2% and 1% respectively. Between the ages of 11 and 15, use of cannabis increases much more quickly with age than does use of Class A drugs.

Young people from an Asian background were only about half as likely to have used drugs as their counterparts in other ethnic groups. **(Tables 10.7, 10.8, Figure 10.3)**

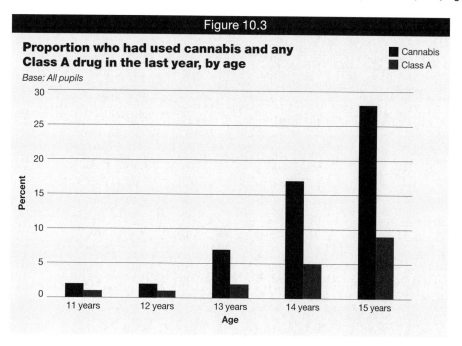

Notes and references

1 The questions about last use of drugs were asked in a grid format (see questionnaire in Appendix C). In calculating whether drugs had been used in the last month, some cases were excluded from the analysis if they met the following criteria – at least one row of the grid incomplete, and among rows that had been completed, none of these drugs had been taken in the last month. A similar system was used to calculate use of drugs in the past year and any use of drugs. There are alternative methods of dealing with cases with non-complete rows, such as assuming that non-completed rows are because pupils have never taken that particular drug. This alternative method would result in slightly lower figures of drug use.

Table 10.1

Whether had heard of individual drugs, by sex: 1999, 2000

All pupils   *England 1999, 2000*

Type of drug	Boys		Girls		Total	
	1999	2000	1999	2000	1999	2000
	%	%	%	%	%	%
Cannabis	90	88	90	88	90	88
Any stimulants	**93**	**89**	**93**	**90**	**93**	**89**
Cocaine	90	86	90	87	90	86
Crack	79	77	76	75	78	76
Ecstasy	76	68	78	71	77	70
Amphetamines	73	65	72	63	72	64
Poppers	40	41	37	41	41	41
Any psychedelics	**78**	**73**	**76**	**71**	**77**	**72**
LSD	67	61	64	58	65	59
Magic mushrooms	67	64	67	64	67	64
Any opiates	**89**	**84**	**91**	**86**	**90**	**85**
Heroin	88	84	90	86	89	85
Methadone	47	37	52	41	49	39
Tranquillisers	59	59	63	61	61	60
Anabolic steroids	53	46	41	35	47	41
Other drugs	2	7	1	5	2	6
Never heard of any of the drugs	5	9	4	8	4	8
Bases	*4520*	*3643*	*4220*	*3389*	*8740*	*7032*

Table 10.2

Whether had heard of individual drugs, by age

All pupils   *England 2000*

Type of drug	Age					
	11 years	12 years	13 years	14 years	15 years	Total
	%	%	%	%	%	%
Cannabis	76	85	91	93	92	88
Any stimulants	**82**	**88**	**91**	**93**	**91**	**89**
Cocaine	76	84	89	91	89	86
Crack	54	68	81	86	86	76
Ecstasy	39	58	75	83	86	70
Amphetamines	30	48	69	81	84	64
Poppers	17	25	37	54	64	41
Any psychedelics	**43**	**60**	**77**	**86**	**88**	**72**
LSD	27	42	61	76	82	59
Magic mushrooms	29	46	68	81	85	64
Any opiates	**75**	**83**	**88**	**90**	**89**	**85**
Heroin	74	82	88	89	89	85
Methadone	22	30	36	49	53	39
Tranquillisers	41	50	60	71	73	60
Anabolic steroids	23	31	40	49	56	41
Other drugs	4	4	5	8	7	6
Never heard of any of the drugs	12	9	7	6	7	8
Bases	*1184*	*1425*	*1429*	*1436*	*1558*	*7032*

Table 10.3

Whether had been offered individual drugs, by sex: 1999, 2000

All pupils   *England 1999, 2000*

Type of drug	Boys		Girls		Total	
	1999	2000	1999	2000	1999	2000
	%	%	%	%	%	%
Cannabis	28	30	25	26	27	28
Any stimulants	**16**	**17**	**15**	**16**	**16**	**17**
Cocaine	7	8	6	7	7	8
Crack	5	6	4	5	5	5
Ecstasy	6	7	6	7	6	7
Amphetamines	7	6	6	5	7	6
Poppers	7	7	5	7	6	7
Any psychedelics	**10**	**10**	**8**	**7**	**9**	**9**
LSD	6	5	4	4	5	4
Magic mushrooms	7	8	6	6	6	7
Any opiates	**5**	**6**	**4**	**6**	**5**	**6**
Heroin	5	6	4	5	4	6
Methadone	1	1	1	1	1	1
Gas, aerosols, glue & other solvents	15	13	16	14	16	13
Tranquillisers	3	2	2	3	2	2
Anabolic steroids	2	2	1	1	1	2
Other drugs	1	2	0	1	0	2
Offered any drugs	36	38	33	34	35	36
Bases	*4506*	*3620*	*4285*	*3365*	*8791*	*6985*

Table 10.4

Whether had been offered individual drugs, by age

All pupils   *England 2000*

Type of drug	Age					
	11 years	12 years	13 years	14 years	15 years	Total
	%	%	%	%	%	%
Cannabis	6	9	23	40	56	28
Any stimulants	**7**	**8**	**13**	**21**	**32**	**17**
Cocaine	5	5	7	9	12	8
Crack	2	3	5	7	9	5
Ecstasy	1	2	4	9	17	7
Amphetamines	2	2	3	6	13	6
Poppers	2	1	4	9	16	7
Any psychedelics	**2**	**4**	**6**	**11**	**18**	**9**
LSD	1	2	3	5	10	4
Magic mushrooms	2	3	6	9	15	7
Any opiates	**3**	**4**	**6**	**7**	**9**	**6**
Heroin	3	4	6	7	8	6
Methadone	1	1	1	1	1	1
Gas, aerosols, glue & other solvents	5	9	12	17	22	13
Tranquillisers	2	1	2	3	4	2
Anabolic steroids	1	1	1	1	3	2
Other drugs	2	1	1	2	2	2
Offered any drugs	15	19	31	47	61	36
Bases	*1169*	*1416*	*1416*	*1429*	*1555*	*6985*

Table 10.5

Whether had used drugs (a) in the last month, (b) in the last year (including in the last month) and (c) ever, by sex and age: 1998-2000[a]

All pupils   *England 1998-2000*

		Age					
		11 years	12 years	13 years	14 years	15 years	Total
		Percentage who had used drugs in the last month					
Boys	1998	-	1	4	11	20	8
	1999	1	2	4	11	20	8
	2000	3	2	6	14	23	10
Girls	1998	-	2	4	9	16	6
	1999	1	2	5	9	16	6
	2000	2	3	5	11	18	8
Total	1998	-	2	4	10	18	7
	1999	1	2	4	10	18	7
	2000	3	3	5	13	21	9
		Percentage who had used drugs in the last year (including those who had done so in the last month)					
Boys	1998	1	4	7	17	30	12
	1999	2	3	7	17	31	12
	2000	3	5	10	20	31	15
Girls	1998	1	3	7	15	26	10
	1999	1	4	9	15	27	11
	2000	3	4	9	19	27	13
Total	1998	1	4	7	16	28	11
	1999	1	4	8	16	29	12
	2000	3	5	9	19	29	14
		Percentage who had ever used drugs					
Boys	1998	1	5	10	19	34	15
	1999	3	5	11	22	38	16
	2000	4	6	12	23	34	17
Girls	1998	1	4	9	17	30	12
	1999	1	5	12	18	33	14
	2000	3	5	12	21	30	15
Total	1998	1	4	10	18	32	14
	1999	2	5	11	20	35	15
	2000	4	6	12	22	32	16
Bases							
Boys	*1998*	*249*	*295*	*249*	*658*	*822*	*2273*
	1999	*873*	*1009*	*943*	*910*	*1034*	*4769*
	2000	*597*	*730*	*715*	*731*	*772*	*3545*
Girls	*1998*	*252*	*306*	*289*	*707*	*739*	*2293*
	1999	*878*	*894*	*919*	*927*	*921*	*4539*
	2000	*556*	*656*	*678*	*676*	*748*	*3314*
Total	*1998*	*501*	*601*	*538*	*1365*	*1561*	*4566*
	1999	*1751*	*1903*	*1862*	*1837*	*1955*	*9308*
	2000	*1153*	*1386*	*1393*	*1407*	*1520*	*6859*

[a] See footnote 1, Chapter 10 Notes and references.

Table 10.6

Whether had used individual drugs in the last year, by sex: 1998-2000

All pupils   *England 1998-2000*

Type of drug	Boys			Girls			Total		
	1998	1999	2000	1998	1999	2000	1998	1999	2000
	Percentage who had used the drug in the last year								
Cannabis	11	11	13	9	10	11	10	11	12
Any stimulants	**3**	**3**	**4**	**3**	**3**	**4**	**3**	**3**	**4**
Cocaine	1	1	1	0	1	1	1	1	1
Crack	0	1	1	0	1	1	0	1	1
Ecstasy	1	1	1	0	1	1	1	1	1
Amphetamines	2	2	1	2	1	1	2	1	1
Poppers	2	1	2	1	1	2	1	2	2
Any psychedelics	**2**	**1**	**2**	**1**	**1**	**1**	**1**	**1**	**2**
LSD	1	1	1	1	1	1	1	1	1
Magic mushrooms	1	1	2	1	1	1	1	1	1
Any opiates	**0**	**0**	**1**	**0**	**0**	**1**	**0**	**0**	**1**
Heroin	0	0	1	0	0	1	0	0	1
Methadone	0	0	0	0	0	0	0	0	0
Gas, aerosols, glue & other solvents	1	2	3	1	3	3	1	3	3
Tranquillisers	0	0	0	0	0	0	0	0	0
Anabolic steroids	1	0	0	0	0	0	0	0	0
Other drugs	1	1	1	1	0	1	1	0	1
Any Class A drug[a]	**3**	**3**	**4**	**3**	**2**	**3**	**3**	**2**	**4**
Used any drug in the last year[b]	**12**	**12**	**15**	**10**	**11**	**13**	**11**	**12**	**14**
Bases	*2287*	*4625*	*3548*	*2360*	*4428*	*3314*	*4647*	*9053*	*6862*

[a] See section 9.4 Definition of Class A drugs.

[b] See footnote 1, Chapter 10 Notes and references.

Table 10.7

Whether had used individual drugs in the last year, by age

All pupils   *England 2000*

Type of drug	Age					
	11 years	12 years	13 years	14 years	15 years	Total
	%	%	%	%	%	%
Cannabis	2	2	7	17	28	12
Any stimulants	**1**	**1**	**2**	**6**	**10**	**4**
Cocaine	1	0	1	1	2	1
Crack	0	0	1	1	2	1
Ecstasy	0	0	0	2	3	1
Amphetamines	0	0	1	2	3	1
Poppers	0	0	1	4	5	2
Any psychedelics	**0**	**1**	**1**	**2**	**4**	**2**
LSD	0	0	0	1	1	1
Magic mushrooms	0	1	1	2	3	1
Any opiates	**0**	**0**	**1**	**1**	**1**	**1**
Heroin	0	0	1	1	1	1
Methadone	0	0	-	0	0	0
Gas, aerosols, glue & other solvents	1	2	3	4	4	3
Tranquillisers	0	0	0	1	0	0
Anabolic steroids	0	0	-	0	0	0
Other drugs	0	0	0	1	1	1
Any Class A drug[a]	**1**	**1**	**2**	**5**	**9**	**4**
Used any drug in the last year[b]	**3**	**5**	**9**	**19**	**29**	**14**
Bases	*1153*	*1386*	*1395*	*1407*	*1521*	*6862*

[a] See section 9.4 Definition of Class A drugs

[b] See footnote 1, Chapter 10 Notes and references.

Table 10.8

Whether had used drugs (a) in the last month, (b) in the last year (including in the last month) and (c) ever, by sex and ethnic group: 1999, 2000[a]

All pupils   *England 1999, 2000*

Drug use		Ethnic group					
		White	Mixed	Asian or Asian British	Black or Black British	Other	Total
		Percentage who had used drugs in the last month					
Boys	1999	8	8	6	9	5	8
	2000	10	12	8	16	11	10
Girls	1999	6	13	3	10	3	6
	2000	9	9	2	8	8	8
Total	1999	7	10	5	9	5	7
	2000	9	11	5	12	10	9
		Percentage who had used drugs in the last year (including those who had done so in the last month)					
Boys	1999	13	11	8	12	8	12
	2000	15	16	10	20	14	15
Girls	1999	12	16	6	13	5	11
	2000	14	13	2	12	10	13
Total	1999	12	13	7	13	7	12
	2000	14	14	6	16	12	14
		Percentage who had ever used drugs					
Boys	1999	16	15	10	18	15	16
	2000	17	19	12	22	17	17
Girls	1999	14	19	8	16	10	14
	2000	16	17	3	14	12	15
Total	1999	15	17	9	17	13	15
	2000	16	18	8	18	15	16
Bases							
Boys	*1999*	*4100*	*182*	*286*	*94*	*73*	*4769*
	2000	*2966*	*146*	*252*	*88*	*71*	*3545*
Girls	*1999*	*3995*	*149*	*225*	*89*	*59*	*4539*
	2000	*2775*	*148*	*231*	*77*	*60*	*3314*
Total	*1999*	*8095*	*331*	*511*	*183*	*132*	*9308*
	2000	*5741*	*294*	*483*	*165*	*131*	*6859*

[a] See footnote 1, Chapter 10 Notes and references.

Table 10.9

Whether had used individual drugs (a) in the last month, (b) in the last year (including in the last month) and (c) ever, by sex

All pupils   *England 2000*

Type of drug	Boys			Girls			Total		
	In last month	In last year	Ever	In last month	In last year	Ever	In last month	In last year	Ever
	%	%	%	%	%	%	%	%	%
Cannabis	8	13	14	7	11	13	8	12	14
Any stimulants	**2**	**4**	**5**	**2**	**4**	**5**	**2**	**4**	**5**
Cocaine	1	1	1	1	1	1	1	1	1
Crack	0	1	1	0	1	1	0	1	1
Ecstasy	1	1	2	1	1	2	1	1	2
Amphetamines	0	1	2	0	1	2	0	1	2
Poppers	1	2	3	1	2	3	1	2	3
Any psychedelics	**1**	**2**	**3**	**1**	**1**	**2**	**1**	**2**	**2**
LSD	0	1	1	0	1	1	0	1	1
Magic mushrooms	1	2	2	1	1	2	1	1	2
Any opiates	**0**	**1**	**1**	**0**	**1**	**1**	**0**	**1**	**1**
Heroin	0	1	1	0	1	1	0	1	1
Methadone	0	0	0	0	0	0	0	0	0
Gas, aerosols, glue & other solvents	2	3	4	1	3	4	2	3	4
Tranquillisers	0	0	1	0	0	0	0	0	0
Anabolic steroids	0	0	0	0	0	0	0	0	0
Other drugs	0	1	1	0	1	1	0	1	1
Any Class A drug[a]	**2**	**4**	**5**	**2**	**4**	**5**	**2**	**4**	**5**
Used any drug[b]	**10**	**15**	**17**	**8**	**13**	**15**	**9**	**14**	**16**
Bases	*3548*	*3548*	*3548*	*3314*	*3314*	*3314*	*6862*	*6862*	*6862*

[a] See section 9.4 Definition of Class A drugs.

[b] See footnote 1, Chapter 10 Notes and references.

11 Health education

Jim Jamison and Ian Schagen

11.1 Introduction

Questions about the content of health education lessons in the last 12 months were first asked of pupils in the 1986 and 1988 surveys. These questions were not included in the 1990 or 1992 surveys, but were re-introduced in 1994 and have been included on every survey since then. The 2000 survey covers lessons on smoking, drinking and drug use, although other survey years have covered a wider range of health related issues.[1]

In 1994 as well as being asked about drugs in general, for the first time pupils were also asked about whether they remembered any lessons covering solvent abuse. From 1996 pupils were asked about lessons covering the specific drugs heroin, crack or cocaine and ecstasy. The 2000 survey repeated these questions. Specifically, pupils were asked whether they remembered having any health education lessons in the last 12 months for each of seven different topics:

- Smoking

- Alcohol

- Heroin

- Crack or cocaine

- Solvent abuse/glue sniffing

- Ecstasy

- Drugs in general

It should be noted that, as in previous years, pupils completed questionnaires in the autumn term. Thus these questions about lessons in the last 12 months would refer predominantly to the previous school year, and that for year 7 pupils this would cover the time when they would have been at primary school.

11.2 Health education lessons in the last year

The proportion of pupils who remembered having lessons on smoking in the last 12 months had increased from 42% in 1986 to a peak of 78% in 1998 and in 2000 stood at 66%. Recall of lessons about alcohol followed a similar pattern with 36% of pupils remembering a lesson about alcohol in 1988, 66% in 1998 and 58% in 2000. Lessons about drugs in general were remembered by 38% of pupils in 1988; this increased to 64% in 1996 and has remained around this level since then. **(Table 11.1, Figure 11.1)**

Pupils who remembered having lessons about either smoking, drinking or drugs were more likely to remember having had lessons about all three of these topics than just having had lessons on one or two of these topics. It is possible that the reason pupils were more likely to recall all three topics may be because the topics are taught together in the same lesson, but it is not possible to tell whether this was the case as this information was not collected as part of the survey.

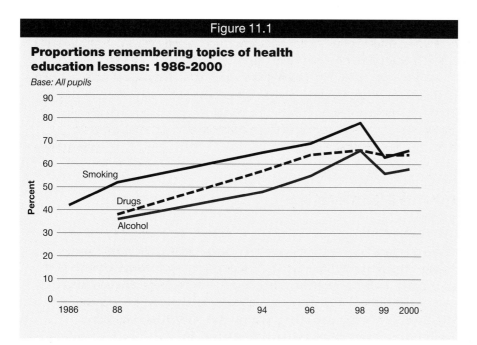

Figure 11.1

Proportions remembering topics of health education lessons: 1986-2000

Base: All pupils

Number of different topic lessons remembered

	%
None	24
One	12
Two	16
All three of smoking, drinking, drugs	48
Base	*6986*

In addition to being asked about recall of lessons about drugs in general, since 1996 pupils have also been asked whether they remember having lessons covering specific drugs. In 2000, lessons about solvents were remembered by a third of pupils (33%), while lessons about heroin, crack or cocaine, and ecstasy were each recalled by around a quarter (25% to 27%). Recall of lessons related to specific drugs fell between 1999 and 2000 for all these four topics, having been fairly constant between 1996 and 1999. **(Table 11.1)**

The same proportions of boys and girls remembered lessons on the topics listed. Older pupils were more likely than younger ones to report having received lessons on the various topics. **(Tables 11.2, 11.3)**

11.3 The association between health education and behaviour

There are two opposing views about the effects of lessons about smoking, drinking or drug use on pupils' behaviour. One view is that if pupils receive lessons about smoking, drinking or drug use, then this may encourage pupils to experiment, rather than dissuade them from trying cigarettes, alcohol or drugs. The alternative view is that ignorance of the effects of smoking, drinking and drug use results in experimentation without understanding what the consequences might be. In theory, an analysis of prevalence of smoking, drinking and use of drugs by whether pupils remembered having lessons about these particular topics would determine whether there was any support for either of these hypotheses. However, there is the complicating factor of age – older children are more likely to remember having lessons on these topics, and older children are more likely to smoke, drink or use drugs. Thus any relationship could be as a result of age differences rather than exposure to topics as part of lessons. This potential confounding effect can be counteracted by standardising to ensure that school year profile (that is, the proportions in each school year) among pupils who remembered having lessons on these topics is the same as the school year profile among those who did not remember having lessons.

There was no significant difference between the prevelance of regular smoking for pupils who remembered lessons about smoking compared to those who did not. Similarly there was also no difference for prevalence of drinking in the last week, or ever trying drugs. The survey asks only whether pupils remembered lessons on these topics, and does not take into account other factors such as frequency and quality of lessons. With this caveat in mind, the findings of this survey do not support the view that having lessons about smoking, drinking or drug use encourages these behaviours, but neither is there any indication that lessons discourage them. **(Tables 11.4-11.6)**

11.4 Schools' smoking policies

In each school involved in the survey, a member of staff was asked about the school's smoking policy and the action that would be taken if pupils were found smoking, drinking alcohol or taking illegal drugs on the premises. A question was also asked about action taken should a pupil be clearly under the influence of alcohol or illegal drugs in school. Replies were received from 218 out of the 225 schools who took part in the survey. The relationship between schools' policies on smoking, drinking and drug use and whether pupils smoke, drink or take drugs is examined in Chapter 13.

Smoking policies for adults

The vast majority of schools (93%) had smoking policies of some kind, covering smoking by adults – teaching staff, non-teaching staff and adult visitors. Responsibility for deciding the smoking policy of the school usually lay with the governors (75%), headteachers (68%) and to a lesser extent the Local Education Authority (25%). Pupils, mentioned by 11% of the schools, were more likely to have some say than parents, mentioned by 6%.

Half the schools (53%) did not allow adults to smoke anywhere on school premises. Half the schools allowed some smoking – around a third allowed smoking outside schools buildings, and a third allowed smoking by adults in certain areas in the buildings (normally in specially designated rooms). In less than one school in ten smoking was allowed in staffrooms or private offices.

In 88% of the schools smoking by adults was prohibited in front of pupils at any time in school hours. The same proportion (88%) reported that the smoking policy applied at all times, not just during school hours.

Smoking, drinking and drug use policies for pupils

The most common action that would be taken by schools if pupils were found smoking, drinking, taking drugs or under the influence of drink or drugs would be to send a letter home. This action would be taken by between 79% and 88% of schools in each of these circumstances. Other actions that would be taken varied depending on what pupils had been found doing.

Schools tended to be more lenient if pupils were found smoking than if they were found drinking or taking drugs. Seventy eight per cent of schools would give the pupil a verbal warning if they were found smoking on school premises and 60% would put a note on the pupil's record. Far fewer schools would refer pupils to a counsellor (14%) or exclude repeat offenders (28%).

If pupils were found drinking alcohol on school premises, verbal warnings (66%) and a note on the pupils record (74%) would still be the more prevalent actions with similar proportions of schools taking these actions as for smoking. In contrast to smoking however, pupils found drinking repeatedly would be more likely to be referred to a counsellor (36%) or excluded (58%).

Actions taken against pupils who were found taking drugs on school premises would be more severe. Sixty nine percent of schools would consider excluding persistent offenders, which is higher than for pupils caught smoking or drinking. The same proportion of schools would put a note on the pupil's record. Schools would also be much more likely to refer a pupil to counselling (63%), than if they were found smoking or drinking. Although a substantial proportion (56%) would still give a verbal warning, this is lower than for smoking or drinking.

Action taken against pupils who were clearly under the influence of drink or drugs (but who were not caught taking either) most closely reflected actions that would be taken if pupils were found taking drugs, except that the proportions of schools who would refer the pupil to a counsellor (51%) or exclude repeat offenders (48%) were lower.

Notes and references

1   When the questions were first introduced in 1986, smoking was asked as a separate category, but drugs in general and alcohol were asked as a combined category. Drugs in general and alcohol were split into separate categories from 1988 onwards.

Table 11.1

Proportion of pupils who remembered receiving health education on various topics in last year: 1986-2000

All pupils   *England 1986-2000*

Health education lessons	Year						
	1986	1988	1994	1996	1998	1999	2000
	%	%	%	%	%	%	%
Drugs:							
Any mention of drugs	a	a	a	67	71	66	64
Heroin	a	a	a	36	36	35	27
Crack/cocaine	a	a	a	34	34	34	26
Ecstasy	a	a	a	41	37	34	25
Solvent abuse/glue sniffing	a	a	33	41	43	40	33
Drugs in general	35b	38	57	64	66	64	61
Smoking	42	52	65	69	78	63	66
Alcohol	35b	36	48	55	66	56	58
Bases	*3189*	*2759*	*2971*	*2705*	*4328*	*9023*	*6986*

[a] Questions on solvent abuse and specific drugs were introduced in 1994 and 1996 respectively.

[b] Drugs and alcohol was a combined answer category in 1986.

Table 11.2

Recall of health education lessons in the last year, by sex

All pupils   *England 2000*

Recall of health education lessons	Sex		
	Boys	Girls	Total
	%	%	%
Drugs:			
Any mention of drugs	65	64	64
Heroin	26	27	27
Crack/cocaine	26	26	26
Ecstasy	25	25	25
Solvent abuse/glue sniffing	34	33	33
Drugs in general	62	60	61
Smoking	66	67	66
Alcohol	58	57	58
Bases	*3614*	*3372*	*6986*

Table 11.3

Recall of health education lessons in the last year, by pupil's current school year[a]

All pupils   *England 2000*

Recall of health education lessons	Current school year					
	Y 7	Y 8	Y 9	Y 10	Y 11	Total
	%	%	%	%	%	%
Drugs:						
Any mention of drugs	47	54	69	76	75	64
Heroin	16	17	29	35	36	27
Crack/cocaine	16	18	29	35	35	26
Ecstasy	9	13	27	36	40	25
Solvent abuse/glue sniffing	23	23	37	40	43	33
Drugs in general	43	51	66	73	72	61
Smoking	49	64	73	74	70	66
Alcohol	42	49	62	69	67	58
Bases	*1385*	*1436*	*1423*	*1430*	*1312*	*6986*

[a] The breakdown is by school year rather than age, as this gives a better indication of the school years in which the lessons concerned took place.

Table 11.4

Regular smokers, by sex and whether remembered having lessons on smoking in the last year (standardised for school year[a])

All pupils   *England 2000*

Sex	Remembered lessons about smoking	
	Yes	No
	Percent regular smokers	
Boys	8	9
Girls	12	14
All pupils	10	11
Bases		
Boys	*2365*	*936*
Girls	*2249*	*827*
All pupils	*4614*	*1763*

[a] In order to control for age differences, the data have been standardised to ensure that the school year profile for those who remembered lessons is the same as the school year profile for those who didn't.

Table 11.6

Ever used drugs, by sex and whether remembered having lessons on drugs in the last year (standardised for school year[a])

All pupils   *England 2000*

Sex	Remembered lessons about drugs	
	Yes	No
	Percent ever had drugs	
Boys	16	18
Girls	16	14
All pupils	16	16
Bases		
Boys	*2287*	*1183*
Girls	*2113*	*1125*
All pupils	*4400*	*2308*

[a] In order to control for age differences, the data have been standardised to ensure that the school year profile for those who remembered lessons is the same as the school year profile for those who didn't.

Table 11.5

Drank last week, by sex and whether remembered having lessons on drinking in the last year (standardised for school year[a])

All pupils   *England 2000*

Sex	Remembered lessons about drinking	
	Yes	No
	Percent who drank last week	
Boys	26	25
Girls	24	24
All pupils	25	24
Bases		
Boys	*2098*	*1126*
Girls	*1911*	*1044*
All pupils	*4009*	*2170*

[a] In order to control for age differences, the data have been standardised to ensure that the school year profile for those who remembered lessons is the same as the school year profile for those who didn't.

12 Smoking, drinking and drug use

Jim Jamison, Ian Schagen, Peter Emery and Richard Boreham

12.1 Introduction

Previous chapters in this report have looked at the individual patterns of use of cigarettes, alcohol and drugs. To summarise, smoking, drinking and use of drugs all increased substantially with age. In addition girls were more likely than boys to smoke, whereas boys were more likely than girls to take drugs. In 2000, there was no difference in the proportion of boys or girls who drank alcohol in the past week, although historically boys had been more likely than girls to do so, and a higher proportion of boys than girls said that they usually drank at least once a week. This chapter investigates the relationship between each of these behaviours.

12.2 Smoking and drinking

Smoking and drinking were highly inter-related. Pupils who drank were more likely to be regular smokers – 33% of pupils who usually drank every week were regular smokers, whereas only 1% of pupils who had never had a drink were regular smokers. Conversely, 57% of regular smokers drank every week compared with 6% of those who had never smoked. This appears to show that smokers were more likely also to drink, than drinkers were to smoke. However this is an artefact caused by the fact that a higher proportion of pupils drank (17%) than smoked (10%).

Among pupils who usually drink at least once a week, girls were more likely than boys to smoke regularly (41% compared with 26%), which is not unexpected, given that girls were more likely to smoke. **(Tables 12.1, 12.2)**

As smoking and drinking behaviour were both strongly related to age, it could be the case that the observed relationship is due to the fact that older pupils were more likely to smoke and drink than younger pupils. However among 15 year olds, those who smoked were more likely than non-smokers to drink at least once a week (67% and 20% respectively), and those who drank at least once a week were more likely than non-drinkers to smoke regularly (39% compared with 6% respectively). This suggests that the relationship between smoking and drinking is not all accounted for by age. **(Tables 12.3, 12.4)**

At age 11, 69% of pupils neither drank nor had ever smoked but by age 15 the equivalent percentage was 11%. Less than 1% of 11 year olds smoked regularly and drank at least weekly, whereas 16% of pupils aged 15 did. **(Table 12.5)**

12.3 Drug use in relation to smoking and drinking

The likelihood of pupils using drugs is closely related to whether or not they smoked. Fifty three per cent of regular smokers had used drugs in the last month compared with 1% of those who had never smoked. For each category of smoking behaviour, older pupils were more likely to have used drugs and boys were more likely than girls to have done so. For all ages, pupils who smoked regularly were most likely to have used drugs.

There was a clear relationship between usual drinking frequency and drug use, though this was less marked than for smoking. Thirty one per cent of those who drank at least once a week had used drugs in the last month, whereas only 2% of those who had never had a drink had used drugs. Within each category of drinking frequency, there was no overall pattern of difference between boys and girls. For all ages, pupils who usually drank once a week or every two weeks were more likely to have used drugs in the last month and in each drinking category, the older pupils (aged 14 and 15) were more likely to have used drugs.

(Tables 12.6-12.9)

Table 12.10 shows the relationship between smoking status, drinking status and proportion of pupils taking drugs in the last month and year. Pupils who were regular smokers and who usually drank at least once a week were the most likely group to have taken drugs in the last month (61%). Drug use was more strongly related to smoking status than drinking status – 30% of regular smokers who drank less than once a month had taken drugs in the last month compared with only 5% of regular drinkers who did not smoke. Only 1% of pupils who had never smoked and drank less than once a month had taken drugs in the last month.

(Table 12.10)

12.4 Assessing the relative importance of different factors to predict whether pupils used drugs

It is clear from the previous sections that drug use is associated with smoking and drinking behaviour in children, as well as to other factors such as sex and age. In order to determine to what extent these factors predict likelihood of taking drugs, a statistical technique called logistic regression (see technical annex) was used. Separate models were run for boys and girls, with age, smoking status and drinking status as independent variables and drug use in the last year as the dependent variable.

It is important to note that this analysis does not infer causality and that models could be run predicting smoking or drinking with drug use as one of the independent variables. However, given that the average age at which children first try drugs is older than the age at which they first experiment with cigarettes or alcohol,[1] it was decided to have drug use as the dependent variable in the models.

Smoking status and drinking status were significant predictors of drug use in the last year for both boys and girls, even when adjusted for age. Whether a pupil was a regular smoker was the strongest predictor of whether they had taken drugs in the last year. The odds of boys, who smoked regularly, taking drugs in the last year were 50 times as high as for boys who had never smoked – independent of their age or their drinking behaviour, and this pattern was also found among girls. Among boys who usually drank at least once a week, their odds of having taken drugs in the last year were five times those of boys who did not drink[2] – for girls the equivalent multiplier was four times.

(Table 12.11)

12.5 Smoking, drinking and drug use among 15 year olds

Defining drinkers as being those who usually drink at least once a week results in more pupils being defined as drinkers than are defined as regular smokers. This can make interpretation difficult as has already been shown in section 12.1 – smokers appeared to be more likely to drink than drinkers were to smoke, although obviously there were the same number of pupils who both drank and smoke. There is also the factor of age that is related to smoking, drinking and drug use and which needs to be taken into account.

In order to examine which of smoking, drinking and drug use are more closely related to each other, definitions need to be chosen such that the groups of smokers, drinkers and drug users are of similar size.[3] Age differences also need to be accounted for. This can be done by using the following groups among 15 year olds only and analysing the prevalence of combinations of each of these behaviours.

- Smoke at least one cigarette a week (23% of 15 year olds)

- Drink at least twice a week (22% of 15 year olds)

- Taken drugs in last month (21% of 15 year olds)

Smoking and drug use were more closely associated with each other than smoking and drinking or than drinking and drug use. Where pupils could be classified into two of the groups, smoking and drug use (7% of pupils) were more closely related than smoking and drinking (3% of pupils), or drinking and drug use (3% of pupils). This pattern was seen for both boys and girls.

Six per cent of 15 year old boys and 7% of 15 year old girls were regular smokers, drank at least twice a week and had taken drugs in the last month. In contrast, 59% of 15 year old boys and 63% of 15 year old girls did not fall into any of these groups. **(Table 12.12)**

Notes and references

1 Goddard E, Higgins V (2000) *Drug use, smoking and drinking among young teenagers in 1999*. Stationery Office. London.

2 This includes those who had never had a proper alcoholic drink, and also those who had but who had answered that they never drank alcohol now.

3 This is so that, for example, the overlap between smoking and drug use can be directly compared to the overlap between drinking and drug use. If there were twice as many drinkers as smokers, then among pupils who took drugs there would probably be a higher proportion that drank than smoked because there were more drinkers in the population. If the proportion of drinkers and smokers are the same, it is possible to compare prevalence of smoking and drinking among pupils who take drugs.

Table 12.1

Smoking behaviour, by sex and usual drinking frequency

All pupils   *England 2000*

Smoking behaviour	Usual drinking frequency					
	Every week	Once a fortnight	Once a month	A few times a year	Doesn't drink	Total
	%	%	%	%	%	%
Boys						
Regular smoker	26	15	11	4	2	9
Occasional smoker	17	13	10	6	3	8
Used to smoke	16	13	11	8	3	8
Tried smoking	20	26	29	26	14	20
Never smoked	22	33	40	57	78	56
Girls						
Regular smoker	41	20	16	7	1	12
Occasional smoker	20	18	18	9	3	10
Used to smoke	12	13	15	9	2	8
Tried smoking	13	25	20	25	13	17
Never smoked	13	25	20	25	13	17
Total						
Regular smoker	33	17	14	5	1	10
Occasional smoker	19	15	14	7	3	9
Used to smoke	14	13	13	8	3	8
Tried smoking	17	26	25	25	13	18
Never smoked	18	28	35	54	80	55
Bases						
Boys	*706*	*287*	*312*	*779*	*1542*	*3626*
Girls	*569*	*291*	*316*	*723*	*1487*	*3386*
Total	*1275*	*578*	*628*	*1502*	*3029*	*7012*

Smoking, drinking and drug use among young people in England in 2000

Table 12.2

Usual drinking frequency, by sex and smoking behaviour

All pupils   *England 2000*

Smoking behaviour		Usual drinking frequency					
		Every week	Once a fortnight	Once a month	A few times a year	Doesn't drink	Bases
Boys							
Regular smoker	%	58	14	11	9	9	316
Occasional smoker	%	44	13	11	16	15	273
Used to smoke	%	38	13	11	20	18	296
Tried smoking	%	19	11	13	28	30	717
Never smoked	%	8	5	6	22	60	2024
Total	**%**	**19**	**8**	**9**	**21**	**43**	**3626**
Girls							
Regular smoker	%	57	14	12	12	4	410
Occasional smoker	%	35	16	17	20	12	332
Used to smoke	%	27	15	18	25	14	256
Tried smoking	%	13	13	11	31	32	579
Never smoked	%	4	4	5	20	67	1809
Total	**%**	**17**	**9**	**9**	**21**	**44**	**3386**
All pupils							
Regular smoker	%	57	14	12	11	6	726
Occasional smoker	%	39	15	14	18	14	605
Used to smoke	%	33	14	14	22	16	552
Tried smoking	%	16	11	12	29	31	1296
Never smoked	%	6	4	6	21	63	3833
Total	**%**	**18**	**8**	**9**	**21**	**43**	**7012**

Table 12.3

Smoking behaviour, by usual drinking frequency among 15 year olds

All pupils aged 15 years   *England 2000*

Smoking behaviour	Usual drinking frequency					Total
	Every week	Once a fortnight	Once a month	A few times a year	Doesn't drink	
	%	%	%	%	%	%
Regular smoker	39	19	17	11	6	23
Occasional smoker	18	14	10	7	4	12
Used to smoke	14	16	13	11	5	12
Tried smoking	13	26	25	26	17	19
Never smoked	16	25	35	46	67	33
Bases	630	238	192	247	249	1556

Table 12.4

Usual drinking frequency, by smoking behaviour among 15 year olds

All pupils aged 15 years   *England 2000*

Usual drinking frequency	Smoking behaviour					Total
	Regular smoker	Occasional smoker	Used to smoke	Tried smoking	Never smoked	
	%	%	%	%	%	%
Every week	67	59	47	28	20	40
Once a fortnight	12	17	20	21	12	15
Once a month	9	10	13	16	13	12
A few times a year	7	9	14	21	22	16
Doesn't drink	4	6	7	14	33	16
Bases	362	193	191	302	508	1556

Table 12.5

Smoking behaviour and usual drinking frequency, by sex and age

All pupils   *England 2000*

Smoking behaviour	Age					
	11 years	12 years	13 years	14 years	15 years	Total
	%	%	%	%	%	%
Boys						
Regular smoker:						
Drinks every week	0	1	2	6	14	5
Drinks less than weekly	1	1	3	4	6	3
Does not drink at all	0	0	1	1	2	1
Ex-smokers, occasional smokers:						
Drinks every week	2	3	8	15	21	10
Drinks less than weekly	7	15	18	23	19	17
Does not drink at all	11	12	9	7	5	8
Has never smoked:						
Drinks every week	1	2	5	5	8	4
Drinks less than weekly	11	18	23	22	16	18
Does not drink at all	67	49	31	17	10	33
Girls						
Regular smoker:						
Drinks every week	0	1	4	10	17	7
Drinks less than weekly	0	1	5	8	8	5
Does not drink at all	-	0	1	1	0	0
Ex-smokers, occasional smokers:						
Drinks every week	2	2	8	9	16	8
Drinks less than weekly	7	14	22	26	24	19
Does not drink at all	10	10	8	8	4	8
Has never smoked:						
Drinks every week	1	1	1	2	5	2
Drinks less than weekly	9	17	17	18	15	16
Does not drink at all	71	54	34	17	11	36
Total						
Regular smoker:						
Drinks every week	0	1	3	8	16	6
Drinks less than weekly	0	1	4	6	7	4
Does not drink at all	0	0	1	1	1	1
Ex-smokers, occasional smokers:						
Drinks every week	2	3	8	12	18	9
Drinks less than weekly	7	14	20	24	21	18
Does not drink at all	10	11	8	7	4	8
Has never smoked:						
Drinks every week	1	1	3	4	6	3
Drinks less than weekly	10	17	20	21	15	17
Does not drink at all	69	51	32	17	11	34
Bases						
Boys	*609*	*743*	*732*	*747*	*795*	*3626*
Girls	*564*	*681*	*693*	*687*	*761*	*3386*
Total	*1173*	*1424*	*1425*	*1434*	*1556*	*7012*

Table 12.6
Drug use, by smoking behaviour and sex

All pupils   *England 2000*

Smoking behaviour	Sex		
	Boys	Girls	Total
	Percentage who had used drugs		
Drug use in last month			
Regular smoker	64	44	53
Occasional smoker	30	20	24
Used to smoke	12	5	9
Tried smoking	5	5	5
Never smoked	1	1	1
Total	**10**	**8**	**9**
Drug use in last year			
Regular smoker	74	60	66
Occasional smoker	44	29	36
Used to smoke	23	14	19
Tried smoking	10	8	9
Never smoked	2	1	2
Total	**15**	**13**	**14**
Bases			
Regular smoker	*303*	*388*	*691*
Occasional smoker	*257*	*313*	*570*
Used to smoke	*279*	*249*	*528*
Tried smoking	*686*	*560*	*1246*
Never smoked	*1981*	*1771*	*3752*
Total	**3506**	**3281**	**6787**

Table 12.8
Drug use, by usual drinking frequency and sex

All pupils   *England 2000*

Usual drinking frequency	Sex		
	Boys	Girls	Total
	Percentage who had used drugs		
Drug use in last month			
At least once a week	31	30	31
About once a fortnight	18	17	18
About once a month	9	10	10
A few times a year	5	3	4
Doesn't drink	2	1	2
Total	**10**	**8**	**9**
Drug use in last year			
At least once a week	42	42	42
About once a fortnight	27	25	26
About once a month	17	18	18
A few times a year	9	6	8
Doesn't drink	3	2	2
Total	**15**	**13**	**14**
Bases			
At least once a week	*673*	*539*	*1212*
About once a fortnight	*279*	*281*	*560*
About once a month	*300*	*311*	*611*
A few times a year	*752*	*696*	*1448*
Doesn't drink	*1495*	*1446*	*2941*
Total	**3499**	**3273**	**6772**

Table 12.7
Drug use, by smoking behaviour and age

All pupils   *England 2000*

Smoking behaviour	Age			
	12-13 years	14 years	15 years	Total
	Percentage who had used drugs			
Drug use in last month				
Regular smoker	35	52	60	53
Occasional smoker	17	26	32	24
Used to smoke	4	8	15	9
Tried smoking	3	6	7	5
Never smoked	1	1	2	1
Total	**4**	**13**	**21**	**9**
Drug use in last year				
Regular smoker	48	67	73	66
Occasional smoker	24	39	49	36
Used to smoke	12	19	27	19
Tried smoking	6	12	12	9
Never smoked	1	2	3	2
Total	**6**	**20**	**29**	**14**
Bases				
Regular smoker	*140*	*204*	*347*	*691*
Occasional smoker	*240*	*146*	*184*	*570*
Used to smoke	*206*	*141*	*181*	*528*
Tried smoking	*635*	*317*	*294*	*1246*
Never smoked	*2674*	*578*	*500*	*3752*
Total	**3895**	**1386**	**1506**	**6787**

Table 12.9

Drug use, by usual drinking frequency and age

All pupils   *England 2000*

Usual drinking frequency	Age			
	11-13 years	14 years	15 years	Total
	Percentage who had used drugs			
Drug use in last month				
At least once a week	19	30	37	31
About once a fortnight	9	18	23	18
About once a month	9	10	10	10
A few times a year	3	5	5	4
Doesn't drink	1	4	5	2
Total	**4**	**13**	**21**	**9**
Drug use in last year				
At least once a week	26	40	50	42
About once a fortnight	14	29	31	26
About once a month	15	22	17	18
A few times a year	6	9	11	8
Doesn't drink	2	6	5	2
Total	**6**	**20**	**29**	**14**
Bases				
At least once a week	*285*	*327*	*600*	*1212*
About once a fortnight	*152*	*174*	*234*	*560*
About once a month	*260*	*165*	*186*	*611*
A few times a year	*840*	*366*	*242*	*1448*
Doesn't drink	*2346*	*353*	*242*	*2941*
Total	***3883***	***1385***	***1504***	***6772***

Table 12.10

Drug use, by smoking behaviour and usual drinking frequency

All pupils   *England 2000*

Smoking behaviour	Usual drinking frequency				
	Every week	Once a fornight	Once a month	Less often/ Never	Total
	Percentage who had used drugs				
Drug use in last month					
Regular smoker	61	53	44	30	52
Occasional smoker	32	36	13	14	24
Used to smoke	18	10	5	2	9
Tried smoking	12	7	5	2	5
Never smoked	5	1	1	1	1
Total	**31**	**18**	**10**	**2**	**9**
Drug use in last year					
Regular smoker	73	69	62	42	66
Occasional smoker	47	47	28	20	36
Used to smoke	35	18	15	7	19
Tried smoking	18	16	10	5	9
Never smoked	7	1	3	1	2
Total	**42**	**26**	**17**	**4**	**14**
Bases					
Regular smoker	*393*	*95*	*81*	*118*	*687*
Occasional smoker	*226*	*85*	*83*	*174*	*568*
Used to smoke	*171*	*74*	*78*	*205*	*528*
Tried smoking	*197*	*147*	*148*	*747*	*1239*
Never smoked	*221*	*159*	*220*	*3132*	*3732*
Total	***1208***	***560***	***610***	***4376***	***6754***

Table 12.11

Odds ratios predicting prevalence of taking drugs in last year

All pupils *England 2000*

Independent variables[a]	Boys			Girls		
	Bases	Odds ratio	95% Confidence Interval	*Bases*	Odds ratio	95% Confidence Interval
Age		P=0.0001			P=0.0362	
11 years	*583*	1.00		*549*	1.00	
12 years	*719*	1.04	(0.54-1.98)	*650*	0.89	(0.44-1.81)
13 years	*703*	1.05	(0.57-1.92)	*665*	0.70	(0.36-1.38)
14 years	*718*	1.89	(1.06-3.38)	*664*	1.09	(0.57-2.08)
15 years	*765*	2.20	(1.24-3.93)	*738*	1.29	(0.68-2.45)
Cigarette smoking status		P=0.0000			P=0.0000	
Regular smoker	*302*	53.81	(35.33-81.94)	*385*	52.48	(30.54-90.19)
Occasional smoker	*257*	18.43	(12.16-27.94)	*311*	17.98	(10.39-31.12)
Used to smoke	*279*	6.86	(4.44-10.60)	*249*	7.28	(3.96-13.39)
Tried smoking	*682*	3.11	(2.06-4.68)	*557*	5.65	(3.24-9.83)
Never smoked	*1968*	1.00		*1764*	1.00	
Usual drinking frequency		P=0.0000			P=0.0000	
At least once a week	*671*	5.31	(3.47-8.15)	*537*	4.13	(2.52-6.77)
About once a fortnight	*279*	3.82	(2.32-6.28)	*281*	3.17	(1.86-5.42)
About once a month	*300*	2.76	(1.65-4.63)	*310*	2.34	(1.36-4.02)
A few times a year	*751*	2.55	(1.62-4.01)	*696*	1.12	(0.66-1.90)
Doesn't drink	*1487*	1.00		*1442*	1.00	

a Separate models for boys and girls were run with age, smoking status and drinking frequency together as independent variables.

Table 12.12

Smoking, drinking and drug use classification among 15 year olds, by sex

All pupils aged 15 years *England 2000*

Smoking, drinking and drug use	Sex		
	Boys	Girls	Total
	%	%	%
Regular smoker, drink twice a week & taken drugs in last month	6	7	6
Regular smoker & drink twice a week only	2	3	3
Regular smoker & taken drugs in last month only	8	6	7
Drink twice a week & taken drugs in last month only	4	2	3
Regular smoker only	4	8	6
Drink twice a week only	11	6	9
Taken drugs in last month only	5	3	4
None of these	59	63	61
Bases	*741*	*720*	*1461*

13 Social and educational factors

Richard Boreham

13.1 Introduction

The central aims of this survey are to measure the prevalence of smoking, drinking and drug use among young people and to monitor trends. The survey is not designed to investigate the causes of these behaviours. There is not scope within the questionnaire to collect, for example, information about pupils' families, friends and local environments. Collection of standard socio-economic measures such as social class is problematic because pupils either do not know what jobs their parents or guardians have, or are unable to provide the relevant detail for detailed social class coding. Proxy measures of social class, such as number of cars owned by the pupil's family, have been tried in the past, but there was evidence of over-reporting and these measures were not felt to be reliable.[1] However, pupils are asked about one indicator of social disadvantage - whether they receive free school meals (or vouchers for free school meals).[2] There were other measures that potentially could have been used in the analysis at an individual level, namely questions about truanting or school exclusion, but these were felt to be measures of behaviour rather than social circumstances. The relationships of truanting and exclusion to smoking, drinking and drug use have been looked at separately.

Other surveys do collect wider information and this chapter gives comparative examples from the Health Survey for England, a household survey. This alternative dataset was examined because the data are able to provide alternative measures of socio-economic status (namely social class and household income) that are too problematic to collect directly from pupils.[3]

In addition to this limited data on individual pupils, a range of information is available about each participating school and its pupils as a whole. It is possible, therefore, to investigate whether smoking, drinking and drug use are related to school characteristics by using a technique called multi-level modelling. The following school level variables were tested to see whether they predicted behaviour.

Type of school	Comprehensive, Secondary Modern, Grammar and Private
English as an Additional Language	Banded into None, < 5% and 5%+ of pupils
GCSE 5 A*-C pass rate	Banded into < 30%, 30%< 60% and 60%+ of pupils
Townsend Deprivation Index	Banded into quintiles. The Townsend Index was used as the deprivation measure as it could be calculated at postcode sector level which is the best approximation to the main catchment area of a school
School size	Banded into < 750 pupils, 750< 1000 pupils and 1000+ pupils
Government Office Region	North East, North West (inc Merseyside), Yorks and Humber, East Midlands, West Midlands, Eastern, London, South East and South West
Eligible for Free School Meals	Banded into < 5%, 5%< 10% and 10%+ of pupils
Sex	Mixed, Boys only and Girls only
Action if child caught smoking on school premises	Exclusion for repeat offenders[4]
Action if child caught drinking on school premises	Exclusion for repeat offenders[4]
Action if child caught taking drugs on school premises	Exclusion for repeat offenders[4]

Models were run separately for three dependent variables: being a regular smoker, drinking in the past week, and using drugs in the last year, and separate models were run for boys and girls. Age is a very strong predictor of smoking, drinking and drug use, and therefore all models were controlled by age. As the focus of this chapter is on social and educational characteristics, the relationship between age and smoking, drinking and drug use is not commented on, but is covered in previous chapters.

Amount of variation in behaviours explained by school level variables

Before models were run with any variables as predictors, null models were run (with no predictor variables) to determine the amount of variation in each of smoking, drinking and drug use that was explained at the individual level and the school level.

Most of the variation in whether pupils are likely to smoke, drink or take drugs is explained by individual level factors. It appears that only around one eighth of the variation is due to school level factors for each of these behaviours, which perhaps is not surprising given the steep increase with age in prevalence of smoking, drinking and drug use that has been shown in other chapters.   **(Table 13.1)**

Testing predictors

A multi-stage iterative analysis was used in order to determine which individual and school level factors predicted the prevalence of each of smoking, drinking and drug use.

First stage models were run for each potential individual level and school level predictor and were controlled for age and ethnicity of pupils (two demographic characteristics which have been shown to have a relationship with smoking, drinking and drug use).

Second stage models were then run containing any factors which were significant predictors from the first set of models (and age and ethnicity), to see whether predictors acted independently or were inter-related.[5]

Results from the second stage models showed that pupils' receipt of free school meals and type of school were the only factors which were significant predictors (once age and ethnicity were all taken into account), although neither was a significant predictor for all of smoking, drinking and drug use. Third stage models were then run with age, ethnicity and receipt of free school meals as individual level characteristics and type of school as a school level characteristic, so that models for smoking, drinking and drug use could be compared.

13.2 The effect of pupils' social characteristics on smoking, drinking or drug use

Pupils' social characteristics were related to smoking, drinking and drug use although the strength and direction of the relationships were different for different behaviours. Pupils who received free school meals were more likely than those who did not receive free school meals to smoke regularly or to have taken drugs in the last year, but there was no difference in prevalence of drinking in the last week between pupils who received free school meals and those who did not.

Evidence from the Health Survey for England showed similar relationships for alternative measures of social characteristics. Prevalence of smoking was higher among those in manual social classes. In contrast, drinking was more prevalent among the highest income groups and showed no relationship with social class.

Boys who received free school meals had higher odds (1.28 compared to average) of being a regular smoker than those who didn't (0.78), and results for girls were similar (see Appendix B for an explanation of odds ratios).   **(Table 13.2, Figure 13.1)**

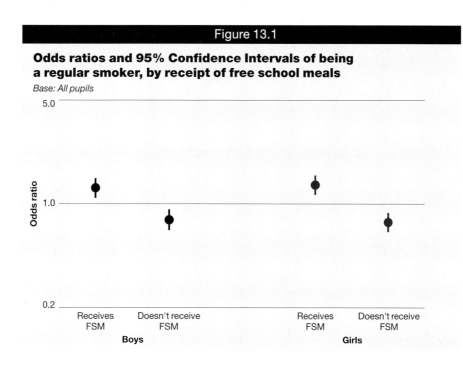

Figure 13.1

**Odds ratios and 95% Confidence Intervals of being
a regular smoker, by receipt of free school meals**

Base: All pupils

Analysis of the same age range of children interviewed as part of the Health Survey for England showed that smoking did not vary by household income, but was higher among manual social classes. **(Tables 13.4, 13.5)**

There was a relationship between whether boys received free school meals and whether they had drunk in the previous week; it was in the opposite direction to the relationship between free school meals and smoking. There was no relationship for girls between receipt of free school meals and drinking. **(Table 13.3, Figure 13.2)**

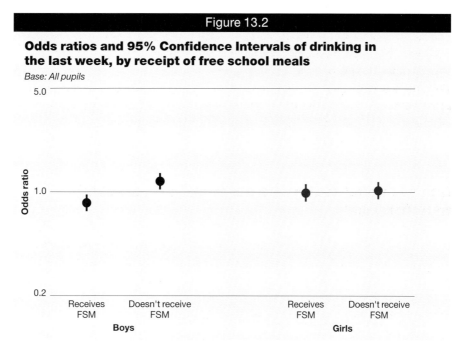

Figure 13.2

**Odds ratios and 95% Confidence Intervals of drinking in
the last week, by receipt of free school meals**

Base: All pupils

Analysis of the same age range of boys interviewed as part of the Health Survey for England showed that prevalence of drinking increased as income increased and was higher in non-manual social classes. The relationship between social characteristics and drinking was weaker among girls. Among girls, drinking was not related to social class, although girls in higher income groups were more likely than those in lower groups to usually drink at least once a week. **(Tables 13.4, 13.5)**

Among boys, uptake of free school meals was not related to having taken drugs in the last year. Girls who received free school meals were slightly more likely (odds ratio 1.30) than those who didn't (odds ratio 0.77) to have taken drugs in the last year. **(Table 13.6, Figure 13.3)**

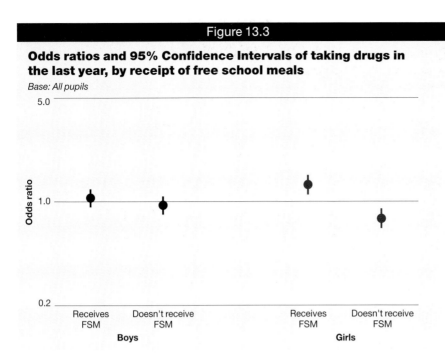

Figure 13.3

Odds ratios and 95% Confidence Intervals of taking drugs in the last year, by receipt of free school meals

Base: All pupils

Research among adults aged 16 and over has shown that smoking prevalence has strong income and class gradients, with those in the lowest income groups and in manual social classes being most likely to smoke. Adults' drinking is related to income and class, although patterns are different for men and women. Women in non-manual social classes and in the highest income groups were more likely to drink more than 14 units of alcohol per week, whereas among men those in the highest income groups were also more likely to drink over 21 units of alcohol per week, but there was no relationship between drinking in the last week and social class.[6]

13.3 Whether the type of school predicts smoking, drinking or drug use

It should be noted that 87% of participating schools were comprehensives, and that there were only a small number of secondary modern (10), grammar (9) and private schools (11) that took part, which is a reflection of the overall proportions of these schools in England. Given the relatively small numbers of non-comprehensive schools, results should be treated with caution.

Despite the relatively small number of secondary modern schools in the sample, pupils at this type of school were more likely to smoke and use drugs even once their age, ethnicity and receipt of free school meals was taken into account. Pupils at private schools were less likely to smoke. The likelihood of pupils drinking alcohol was not related to the type of school.   **(Tables 13.2, 13.3, 13.6, Figures 13.4 , 13.5)**

13.4 Relative importance of school level and individual level social and educational characteristics

Despite the different range of school-level predictors, very little of the variation in pupils smoking, drinking or drug use is explained by the factors at the school level. Social factors at the pupil level do explain some of the variation, although other factors such as age were more important predictors of behaviour. This does not necessarily mean that social factors are not important, but may be a reflection of the difficulty in collecting reliable and valid information about individual pupils' social characteristics. There may be factors such as the behaviour and attitudes of close friends which also influence pupils' decisions about whether to smoke, drink or take drugs.

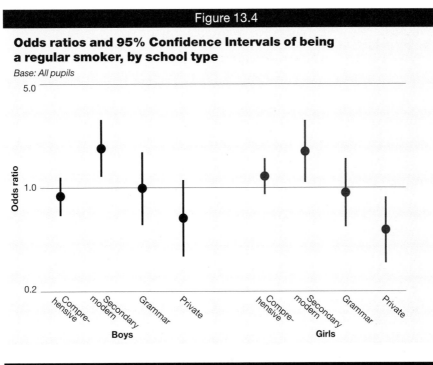

Figure 13.4

Odds ratios and 95% Confidence Intervals of being a regular smoker, by school type

Base: All pupils

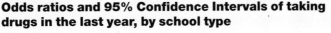

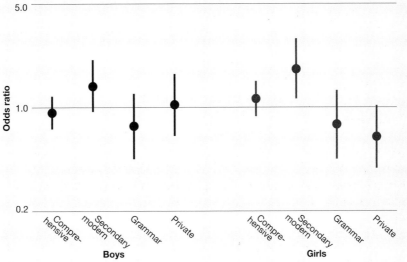

Figure 13.5

Odds ratios and 95% Confidence Intervals of taking drugs in the last year, by school type

Base: All pupils

13.5 Pupils who truant or who have been excluded

Pupils were asked whether they had ever played truant or been excluded from school. Levels of truancy and exclusion described here are thus self-reported, and should be viewed with some caution.

Boys aged 15 were much more likely to have played truant or been excluded than those aged 11. Thirty three percent of 15 year old boys had truanted and 17% had been excluded compared with 6% and 4% respectively among 11 year old boys. There was a similar pattern for girls, although generally girls were less likely to have played truant or been excluded than boys. As age is strongly related to truanting and exclusion, it is necessary to ensure that age does not confound any analysis of smoking, drinking and drug use by truanting and exclusion. Therefore age standardisation was used to ensure that the age profiles of those who had played truant was the same as those who had not, and similarly for the analysis of school exclusion. It is important to note that pupils who truant or are excluded are less likely to be included in the interviewed sample, than those who did not, although the response rate among pupils was high (87%).

The wealth and complexity of factors impacting on the behaviours in question mean that it is difficult to establish the exact nature of any relationship between smoking, drinking and drug use and playing truant or being excluded. However, smoking, drinking and drug use were much more prevalent among both boys and girls who had ever played truant than those who had not. Similar differences were found between pupils who had been excluded and those who had not been. It is not possible from these data to tell if playing truant or being excluded causes smoking, drinking or drug use, or if those who were already smoking, drinking or taking drugs are likely to start playing truant or to be excluded.

(Tables 13.7, 13.8)

Notes and references

1 See Goddard and Higgins (2000) p31 *Drug use, smoking and drinking among young teenagers in 1999* for a fuller discussion.

2 Data on free school meals is usually gathered on the basis of eligibility; however, this survey asks whether pupils receive free school meals rather than whether they are eligible.

3 The Health Survey for England is conducted face-to-face and in people's homes in England only and the data analysed was collected from 1995 to 1997. Although the method of data collection and interviewing time period are different from this survey, it is reasonable to compare in broad terms the relationships between different socio-economic measures captured in the different surveys and smoking and drinking.

4 Exclusion for repeat offenders was one of a number of measures that could be taken by schools if pupils were caught smoking, drinking or taking drugs on school premises. It was the only action taken to be included in the analysis as it was the most severe action that a school could take.

5 Some measures were likely to be inter-related: for example there were no private schools which had any pupils with English as an Additional Language, or that had pupils who were entitled to free school meals.

6 Boreham R et al (1999) *Risk factors for cardiovascular disease* in Erens B & Primatesta P *Health Survey for England: Cardiovascular Disease '98*. The Stationery Office. London.

Table 13.1

Variation in behaviours explained at the school level for null models (uncontrolled)

All pupils   *England 2000*

	Variance at school level	95% Confidence Interval of variance
Boys		
Regular smoker	13%	(0%-24%)
Drank in last week	17%	(10%-23%)
Used drugs in last year	11%	(1%-19%)
Girls		
Regular smoker	19%	(7%-28%)
Drank in last week	14%	(6%-21%)
Used drugs in last year	16%	(4%-25%)

Table 13.2

Odds ratios predicting prevalence of being a regular smoker, by sex

All pupils   *England 2000*

Independent variables[a]	**Boys**			**Girls**		
	Bases	Odds ratio	95% Confidence Interval	*Bases*	Odds ratio	95% Confidence Interval
Receives free school meals[b]						
Yes	566	1.28	(1.10-1.50)	507	1.34	(1.15-1.55)
No	2879	0.78	(0.66-0.91)	2723	0.75	(0.64-0.87)
School type						
Comprehensive	188	0.88	(0.65-1.18)	190	1.19	(0.90-1.58)
Secondary Modern	9	1.85	(1.19-2.86)	8	1.75	(1.09-2.82)
Grammar	5	0.99	(0.56-1.74)	5	0.92	(0.55-1.56)
Private	6	0.62	(0.34-1.13)	10	0.52	(0.31-0.87)
Age						
11 years	558	0.38	(0.24-0.61)	518	0.06	(0.02-0.18)
12 years	701	1.21	(0.87-1.68)	641	0.41	(0.25-0.68)
13 years	692	2.42	(1.82-3.22)	667	1.65	(1.14-2.38)
14 years	725	1.19	(0.86-1.64)	659	3.98	(2.83-5.61)
15 years	769	2.42	(1.82-3.22)	745	6.18	(4.43-8.62)
Ethnic group						
White	2889	1.19	(0.86-1.64)	2723	2.65	(1.76-3.97)
Mixed	150	1.29	(0.76-2.21)	146	3.03	(1.74-5.29)
Asian	246	0.70	(0.43-1.15)	223	0.24	(0.10-0.58)
Black	92	0.97	(0.49-1.92)	81	0.51	(0.19-1.38)
Other	68	0.96	(0.43-2.13)	57	1.00	(0.40-2.49)

[a] All independent variables were entered into one model.

[b] There were 343 pupils who did not answer the question about whether they received free school meals and they have been excluded from the analysis.

Table 13.3

Odds ratios predicting prevalence of drinking in last week, by sex

All pupils   *England 2000*

Independent variables[a]	Boys			Girls		
	Bases	Odds ratio	95% Confidence Interval	*Bases*	Odds ratio	95% Confidence Interval
Receives free school meals[b]						
Yes	*566*	0.84	(0.74-0.96)	*506*	0.98	(0.86-1.12)
No	*2864*	1.19	(1.04-1.35)	*2718*	1.02	(0.89-1.17)
School type						
Comprehensive	*188*	0.91	(0.72-1.13)	*190*	0.97	(0.77-1.23)
Secondary Modern	*9*	0.82	(0.57-1.19)	*8*	0.90	(0.58-1.40)
Grammar	*5*	0.92	(0.60-1.41)	*5*	1.04	(0.66-1.63)
Private	*6*	1.46	(0.97-2.20)	*10*	1.10	(0.75-1.61)
Age						
11 years	*551*	0.23	(0.17-0.31)	*512*	0.20	(0.14-0.28)
12 years	*694*	0.50	(0.40-0.62)	*638*	0.48	(0.38-0.61)
13 years	*692*	0.85	(0.71-1.03)	*667*	1.13	(0.94-1.37)
14 years	*724*	2.18	(1.85-2.57)	*662*	2.16	(1.81-2.59)
15 years	*769*	4.78	(4.08-5.60)	*745*	4.33	(3.66-5.12)
Ethnic group						
White	*2879*	2.04	(1.59-2.62)	*2718*	3.02	(2.21-4.14)
Mixed	*147*	1.72	(1.15-2.57)	*147*	2.94	(1.89-4.59)
Asian	*244*	0.20	(0.12-0.34)	*220*	0.24	(0.12-0.46)
Black	*92*	0.89	(0.52-1.54)	*82*	0.78	(0.40-1.52)
Other	*68*	1.59	(0.92-2.75)	*57*	0.61	(0.27-1.35)

[a] All independent variables were entered into one model.

[b] There were 343 pupils who did not answer the question about whether they received free school meals and they have been excluded from the analysis.

Table 13.4

Prevalence of smoking and drinking, by income and sex (Health Survey for England 1997)[a]

All children aged 11-15 years   *HSE (England) 1997*

Regular smoker/drank in last week	Equalised household income tertile			
	<£8,000	£8,000 <£16,000	£16,000+	Total
	%	%	%	%
Boys				
Usually smokes at least one cigarette a week	8	5	5	6
Usually drinks at least once a week	10	12	16	12
Girls				
Usually smokes at least one cigarette a week	6	6	9	7
Usually drinks at least once a week	4	9	14	9
All pupils				
Usually smokes at least one cigarette a week	7	6	7	7
Usually drinks at least once a week	7	10	15	10
Bases				
Boys	*300*	*355*	*345*	*1119*
Girls	*300*	*309*	*352*	*1097*
Total	*600*	*664*	*697*	*2216*

[a] Reanalysis of Health Survey for England data.

Table 13.5

Prevalence of smoking and drinking, by social class and sex (Health Survey for England 1995-97)[a]

All children aged 11-15 years   *HSE (England) 1995-97*

Regular smoker/drank in last week	Social class of chief income earner		
	Non-manual	Manual	Total
	%	%	%
Boys			
Usually smokes at least one cigarette a week	5	8	6
Usually drinks at least once a week	12	9	11
Girls			
Usually smokes at least one cigarette a week	7	10	8
Usually drinks at least once a week	8	8	8
All pupils			
Usually smokes at least one cigarette a week	6	9	7
Usually drinks at least once a week	10	8	9
Bases			
Boys	*1115*	*1156*	*2377*
Girls	*1105*	*1086*	*2294*
Total	*2220*	*2242*	*4671*

[a] Reanalysis of Health Survey for England data.

Table 13.6

Odds ratios predicting prevalence of taking drugs in last year, by sex

All pupils   *England 2000*

Independent variables[a]	Boys			Girls		
	Bases	Odds ratio	95% Confidence Interval	*Bases*	Odds ratio	95% Confidence Interval
Receives free school meals[b]						
Yes	*541*	1.06	(0.92-1.22)	*484*	1.30	(1.12-1.51)
No	*2805*	0.94	(0.82-1.09)	*2669*	0.77	(0.66-0.89)
School type						
Comprehensive	*188*	0.92	(0.71-1.19)	*190*	1.14	(0.86-1.50)
Secondary Modern	*9*	1.39	(0.93-2.08)	*8*	1.81	(1.14-2.88)
Grammar	*5*	0.75	(0.45-1.24)	*5*	0.77	(0.45-1.31)
Private	*6*	1.04	(0.65-1.67)	*10*	0.63	(0.39-1.02)
Age						
11 years	*541*	0.27	(0.18-0.40)	*508*	0.25	(0.16-0.39)
12 years	*683*	0.46	(0.34-0.62)	*617*	0.40	(0.28-0.57)
13 years	*671*	0.90	(0.70-1.15)	*653*	0.99	(0.76-1.29)
14 years	*704*	2.20	(1.80-2.68)	*647*	2.47	(1.98-3.08)
15 years	*747*	4.06	(3.38-4.88)	*728*	4.11	(3.35-5.05)
Ethnic group						
White	*2821*	0.96	(0.75-1.23)	*2663*	1.87	(1.35-2.60)
Mixed	*139*	1.23	(0.80-1.90)	*142*	1.95	(1.17-3.24)
Asian	*235*	0.50	(0.33-0.76)	*216*	0.22	(0.10-0.48)
Black	*85*	1.65	(1.01-2.70)	*75*	1.22	(0.64-2.33)
Other	*66*	1.03	(0.57-1.88)	*57*	1.02	(0.48-2.18)

[a] All independent variables were entered into one model.

[b] There were 343 pupils who did not answer the question about whether they received free school meals and they have been excluded from the analysis.

Table 13.7

Smoking, drinking and drug use, by age-standardised whether pupils had ever truanted and sex

All pupils *England 2000*

Smoking, drinking and drug use	Ever truanted	
	Yes	No
	%	%
Boys		
Regular smoker	23	4
Drank in last week	39	21
Used drugs in last year	32	9
Girls		
Regular smoker	33	7
Drank in last week	44	19
Used drugs in last year	34	7
Bases		
Boys	*683*	*2898*
Girls	*606*	*2740*

Table 13.8

Smoking, drinking and drug use, by age-standardised whether pupils had ever been excluded and sex

All pupils *England 2000*

Smoking, drinking and drug use	Ever excluded	
	Yes	No
	%	%
Boys		
Regular smoker	23	7
Drank in last week	36	23
Used drugs in last year	27	13
Girls		
Regular smoker	36	11
Drank in last week	43	23
Used drugs in last year	38	12
Bases		
Boys	*377*	*3225*
Girls	*121*	*3250*

14 Comparison of smoking, drinking and drug use in England and Scotland

Kerstin Hinds

14.1 Introduction

Comparing results for England and Scotland requires some care since the age distributions of the two samples are different. This is due to the different education systems in the two countries. In England, pupils transfer to secondary school a year earlier than in Scotland, (most are aged 11 rather than 12), and transfer is usually based on the child's age at the beginning of the school year, rather than on 1st March.

The different structures of the two samples mean that direct comparison between respondents of all ages in the two countries may be misleading, as pupils in the sample in England are mostly aged 11-15 whereas those in the sample in Scotland are mostly aged 12-15. **(Table 14.1)**

In this chapter, we therefore mainly focus on *only those aged 12, 13, 14 or 15* at the time of interview in the two countries and leave out those who were older or younger. The mean age of those in each age group[1] is then very similar for the English and Scottish samples. However, there is an additional complication in that the English sample comprises comparatively more 15 year olds than the Scottish sample (in England, 24% of pupils aged 12-15 are 15, while in Scotland only 18% are 15). This chapter takes account of this difference by 'age-standardising' the data – that is, adjusting the analysis so that pupils at each age account for the same proportion of the whole sample. Thus when total figures are given, in this chapter, each of the four age categories, 12, 13, 14 and 15 represent 25% of the total in both England and Scotland.

Employing this age standardisation technique means that total figures here may vary from those in other chapters in this report. All figures reported in this Chapter are age-standardised apart from those in section 14.5.

In previous reports, adjustments to reflect the different age-profiles of the English and Scottish samples have not been made and '11-15' year olds in England (including more 16 year olds and 11 year olds) have simply been compared with '12-15' year olds in Scotland. As well as the more accurate comparison between the countries for 2000, the present report also includes headline comparisons using the previous method, so that changes over time can be identified. This section on trends is at the end of the chapter (section 14.5).

One further factor that might affect comparison between the English and Scottish samples, would be different fieldwork periods relative to the school year. In both countries fieldwork took place from September to December, but it was staggered to reflect the fact that the English schools began the year in September whereas Scottish school children began their school year in August. As a result 3% of fieldwork in England compared with 15% of fieldwork in Scotland was completed in September. Even with this staggered start in both countries the majority of fieldwork took place in October (61% in England and 56% in Scotland). We judge that the data are comparative in this regard.

14.2 Smoking

As described in Chapter 2, pupils' smoking status was classified using a question on prevalence of smoking and a diary record of cigarettes smoked in the past week. Regular smokers were those who said they generally smoked at least one cigarette each week, occasional smokers said they smoked sometimes, or said they did not now smoke but in the diary reported having had cigarettes in the past week. In 2000, 12% of pupils aged 12-15 in both England and Scotland smoked regularly. Among those aged 15 the proportion of regular smokers was higher in England than in Scotland (23% compared with 19%) while for all other age groups there were no significant differences between the two countries. A higher proportion of pupils in England than in Scotland were classified as occasional smokers (10% compared with 8%).   **(Tables 14.2, 14.3)**

Despite the similar smoking status of pupils in England and Scotland, in 2000 there were some differences in the behaviour reported by pupils who smoked (whether regularly or occasionally). In England, smokers were more likely to have had their first cigarette at a older age. A quarter of pupils who smoked in England (26%) said they had first tried smoking aged 10 or under, compared with a third of those in Scotland (35%).

Smokers in England were also less likely to smoke heavily than their Scottish counterparts. Fifteen per cent of smokers aged 12-15 in England smoked 10 or more cigarettes per day in the last week compared with 20% of those in Scotland.   **(Table 14.4)**

Teenage smokers in England had more difficulty buying cigarettes in shops than their Scottish counterparts, as smokers in England were less likely to attempt to buy from a shop and those that did so were more likely to be refused. Two thirds of pupils in England who smoked had tried to buy cigarettes in a shop in the past year (68%), while in Scotland nearly three quarters of these pupils had tried this (73%). Just over a half of smokers in England who had tried to buy cigarettes in a shop in the past year had been refused service during this time (53%), a slightly higher proportion than in Scotland (48%). English smokers also purchased cigarettes from shops much less frequently. In England 21% of smokers who had tried to buy cigarettes from a shop said they bought cigarettes from a shop almost every day, compared with 37% in Scotland.   **(Table 14.5)**

In England 31% of pupils who smoked sometimes bought cigarettes from a vending machine; in Scotland 27% did so.

Family attitudes towards smoking were similar in England and Scotland. There was no difference in the proportion of pupils who said their parents did not know they smoked in the two countries, nor in the reactions of those parents who did know their children smoked. Children who did not smoke were asked what their parents would do if they did smoke, and again there were no notable differences between England and Scotland (tables not shown). Chapter 5 of this report shows these findings for England in detail.

14.3 Drinking in the previous week

Pupils in England were a little more likely to report having drunk alcohol in the previous week than those in Scotland. Just over a quarter (27%) of those aged 12-15 in England had drunk alcohol in past week compared with just under a quarter (24%) of those in Scotland. These differences between the countries were found for both boys and girls. In both countries boys and girls were equally likely to have drunk alcohol in the past week in 2000.

Turning to look at the amount pupils had drunk, those who had drunk alcohol in the past week in England were likely to have consumed fewer units than their Scottish counterparts. Twenty three per cent of those in England had consumed 14 or more units in the past week compared with 28% of those in Scotland.   **(Tables 14.6, 14.7)**

14.4 **Drug use**

Pupils aged 12-15 in England were marginally less likely than their Scottish counterparts to report having been offered drugs. In total 38% of the English pupils had been offered drugs compared with 40% of those in Scotland.

(Table 14.8)

However, there was no difference in drug use between the two countries; those aged 12-15 in England were no less likely to have used drugs than those in Scotland. Ten per cent of those in England and 12%[2] of those in Scotland had used drugs in the last month and 16% and 17% respectively had done so in the last year. On the whole there were no differences between English and Scottish pupils in the proportions using drugs for either boys or girls or for different age groups. The one exception was 14 year old boys, who in England were less likely to have reported using drugs in the last year than their Scottish counterparts, although this may be a statistical aberration.

(Table 14.9)

There were no differences between pupils in England and those in Scotland in the individual drugs used in the past year.

(Table 14.10)

14.5 **Trend data for England and Scotland**

Comparing differences between England and Scotland in 2000 with those in 1998 and previous years, we do not use the age standardised figures, but rather compare directly between the samples in the two countries. Thus comparisons in this section are between pupils aged 11-15 in England and 12-15 in Scotland.

Smoking

The proportion of pupils reported as being regular smokers was still found to be the same in England and Scotland in 2000, even though the age-profiles were slightly different in each country. Without age standardisation, the total figures include a smaller proportion of older children and thus the overall percentage in both countries was 10% (as compared with 12% with age standardisation). Historically, England had a lower proportion of regular smokers than Scotland, however this gap has been narrowing for some time and apparent differences have not been statistically significant in recent years. It would now appear that levels of regular smoking are generally the same in the two countries.

(Table 14.11)

Use of alcohol

Comparing alcohol use in England and Scotland over time, it appears that similar trends are at play. The proportion of pupils consuming alcohol in the previous week in both countries rose through the first half of the 1990s (although the rise was more dramatic in Scotland), peaking in 1996. There was then a large fall in 1998 and there has been a smaller rise in 2000. In every year higher proportions of pupils in England than in Scotland have reported drinking in the last week. The current position is that 24% of all pupils in English schools and 21% of those in Scottish schools report drinking in the last week.

(Table 14.12)

Drug use

Over the limited time for which data are available (1998-2000), it appears that drug use in England has risen slightly while that in Scotland has remained stable. Levels of drug use in the last year and the last month no longer show any significant difference between the two countries, while in 1998 such differences were found. For example, in 1998 11% of pupils in England and 15% of those in Scotland reported having used drugs in the last year. By 2000 the corresponding figures were 14% and 14%.

(Table 14.13)

Notes and references

1 For example 14 year olds consist of all those who were 14 at their last birthday.

2 Significance tests were carried out on percentages to one decimal place.

Table 14.1

Age profile, by sex and country

All pupils   *England and Scotland 2000*

Age	England			Scotland		
	Boys	Girls	Total	Boys	Girls	Total
	%	%	%	%	%	%
10 years	0	0	0	-	-	-
11 years	17	17	17	8	8	8
12 years	21	20	20	26	26	26
13 years	20	20	20	26	24	25
14 years	21	20	20	23	25	24
15 years	18	20	19	17	17	17
16 years	3	3	3	0	0	0
17 years	-	0	0	-	-	-
Mean age	13.13	13.14	13.13	13.17	13.17	13.17
Standard error of the mean	0.02	0.02	0.02	0.02	0.03	0.02
Bases	*3672*	*3417*	*7089*	*2439*	*2335*	*4774*

Table 14.2

Age-standardised regular cigarette smoking, by age, sex and country[a]

All pupils aged 12-15 years   *England and Scotland 2000*

Age	England			Scotland		
	Boys	Girls	Total	Boys	Girls	Total
	Percentage who smoke regularly					
12 years	2	2	2	3	2	3
13 years	6	10	8	5	10	8
14 years	11	19	15	12	22	17
15 years	21	26	23	15	24	19
Total	10	14	12	9	15	12
Bases						
12 years	*751*	*686*	*1437*	*630*	*610*	*1240*
13 years	*736*	*697*	*1433*	*628*	*560*	*1188*
14 years	*752*	*688*	*1440*	*556*	*586*	*1142*
15 years	*669*	*666*	*1335*	*419*	*386*	*805*
Total	*2908*	*2737*	*5645*	*2233*	*2142*	*4375*

[a] Figures in this table are age-standardised and may therefore differ from findings elsewhere in the report.

Table 14.3

Age-standardised cigarette smoking status, by country[a]

All pupils aged 12-15 years   *England and Scotland 2000*

Smoking status	England	Scotland
	%	%
Regular smoker	12	12
Occasional smoker	10	8
Used to smoke	9	10
Tried once	20	21
Never smoked	50	49
Bases	*5645*	*4375*

[a] Figures in this table are age-standardised and may therefore differ from findings elsewhere in the report.

Table 14.4

Age-standardised smoker type, by country[a]

Regular and occasional smokers aged 12-15 years   *England and Scotland 2000*

Number of cigarettes smoked in last week	England	Scotland
	%	%
Light smoker (0-2/ day)	52	49
Medium smoker (3-9/ day)	33	31
Heavy smoker (10 or more/ day)	15	20
Bases	*1206*	*812*

[a] Figures in this table are age-standardised and may therefore differ from findings elsewhere in the report.

Table 14.5

Age-standardised availability of cigarettes, by country[a]

Regular and occasional smokers aged 12-15 years   *England and Scotland 2000*

Cigarette purchasing	England	Scotland
	%	%
Tried to buy cigarettes in shop in past year	68	73
Bases	1206	812
If tried to buy, frequency of buying cigarettes from shop		
Almost every day	21	37
Once or twice a week	33	23
Two or three times a month	14	14
About once a month	13	9
Only a few times a year	20	16
If tried to buy, whether refused cigarettes in past year		
Yes	53	48
Bases	809	577

[a] Figures in this table are age-standardised and may therefore differ from findings elsewhere in the report.

Table 14.6

Age-standardised frequency of drinking alcohol, by sex and country[a]

All pupils aged 12-15 years   *England and Scotland 2000*

Frequency of drinking alcohol	England			Scotland		
	Boys	Girls	Total	Boys	Girls	Total
	%	%	%	%	%	%
Drank alcohol in last week	29	26	27	24	23	24
Drank alcohol in last 4 weeks, but not last week	15	18	16	16	19	18
Drank alcohol in last 6 months, but not last month	12	12	12	13	14	13
Drank alcohol less recently	11	10	11	13	10	12
Never drank alcohol	33	33	33	33	34	34
Bases	2895	2734	5629	2211	2134	4345

[a] Figures in this table are age-standardised and may therefore differ from findings elsewhere in the report.

Table 14.7

Age-standardised mean units of alcohol drunk in last week, by sex and country[a]

Those who drank last week aged 12-15 years   *England and Scotland 2000*

Alcohol consumption (units)	England			Scotland		
	Boys	Girls	Total	Boys	Girls	Total
	%	%	%	%	%	%
Less than 1 unit over the week	6	7	6	5	6	5
1 unit, less than 7 units	43	48	46	38	43	41
7 units, less than 14 units	23	26	24	25	29	27
14 units or more	28	19	23	33	23	28
Bases	812	711	1523	501	465	966

[a] Figures in this table are age-standardised and may therefore differ from findings elsewhere in the report.

Table 14.8

Age-standardised whether had been offered drugs, by age, sex and country[a]

All pupils aged 12-15 years   *England and Scotland 2000*

Age	England			Scotland		
	Boys	Girls	Total	Boys	Girls	Total
	Percentage who had been offered drugs					
12 years	21	16	19	20	15	18
13 years	30	30	30	38	35	36
14 years	47	45	46	57	50	54
15 years	62	58	60	65	61	63
Total	40	37	38	43	38	40
Bases						
12 years	753	687	1440	631	613	1244
13 years	742	698	1440	629	560	1189
14 years	754	691	1445	559	588	1147
15 years	669	668	1337	421	387	808
Total	2918	2744	5662	2240	2148	4388

[a] Figures in this table are age-standardised and may therefore differ from findings elsewhere in the report.

Table 14.9

Age-standardised whether had used drugs (a) in the last month, (b) in the last year (including the last month) and (c) ever, by age, sex and country[a]

All pupils aged 12-15 years   *England and Scotland 2000*

Age	England			Scotland		
	Boys	Girls	Total	Boys	Girls	Total
	Percentage using drugs					
Used drugs in the last month						
12 years	2	3	3	2	1	2
13 years	6	5	5	8	7	8
14 years	14	11	13	19	12	15
15 years	23	18	21	24	20	22
Total	11	9	10	13	10	12
Used drugs in the last year						
12 years	5	4	5	5	2	3
13 years	10	9	9	12	10	11
14 years	20	19	20	25	19	22
15 years	31	26	29	32	27	30
Total	16	14	16	19	15	17
Ever used drugs						
12 years	6	5	6	6	3	4
13 years	12	12	12	15	11	13
14 years	23	21	22	30	23	27
15 years	34	29	31	34	31	33
Total	19	17	18	22	17	19
Bases						
12 years	729	656	1385	607	606	1213
13 years	714	678	1392	618	554	1172
14 years	731	674	1405	546	578	1124
15 years	648	653	1301	412	384	796
Total	2822	2661	5483	2183	2122	4305

[a] Figures in this table are age-standardised and may therefore differ from findings elsewhere in the report.

Table 14.10

Age-standardised drugs used in the last year, by sex and country[a]

All pupils aged 12-15 years   *England and Scotland 2000*

Type of drug	England			Scotland		
	Boys	Girls	Total	Boys	Girls	Total
	%	%	%	%	%	%
Cannabis	14	12	13	17	13	15
Any stimulants						
Cocaine	1	1	1	1	1	1
Crack	1	1	1	1	0	1
Ecstasy	1	1	1	2	2	2
Amphetamines	1	1	1	2	1	1
Poppers	2	2	2	1	1	1
Any stimulant	5	4	5	4	4	4
Any psychedelics						
LSD	1	1	1	1	1	1
Magic Mushrooms	2	1	2	3	1	2
Any psychedelic	3	1	2	4	2	3
Any opiates						
Heroin	1	1	1	1	1	1
Methadone	0	0	0	0	0	0
Any opiate	1	1	1	1	1	1
Gas, aerosols, glue, & other solvents	3	3	3	4	3	4
Tranquilisers	0	0	0	1	1	1
Anabolic Steroids	0	0	0	0	0	0
Other drugs	1	0	1	0	0	0
Any class A drugs	**5**	**4**	**4**	**5**	**4**	**5**
Used any drug in the last year	16	14	16	19	15	17
Bases	*2804*	*2638*	*5442*	*2165*	*2102*	*4267*

[a] Figures in this table are age-standardised and may therefore differ from findings elsewhere in the report.

Table 14.11

Prevalence of smoking, by sex and country: 1982-2000[a]

All pupils   *England and Scotland 1982-2000*

Survey year	England			Scotland		
	11-15 years			12-15 years		
	Boys	Girls	Total	Boys	Girls	Total
	Percentage who were classified as regular smokers					
1982	11	11	11	15	14	15
1984	13	13	13	16	17	16
1986	7	12	10	10	14	12
1988	7	9	8	b	b	b
1990	9	11	10	11	12	12
1992	9	10	10	10	13	11
1994	10	13	12	11	13	12
1996	11	15	13	14	15	14
1998	9	12	11	11	13	12
2000	9	12	10	8	13	10
Bases (2000)	*3654*	*3407*	*7061*	*2431*	*2327*	*4758*

[a] Figures in this table are **not** age-standardised.

[b] Data were not collected in 1988 in Scotland.

Table 14.12

Prevalence of drinking in the last week, by sex and country: 1990–2000[a]

All pupils					England and Scotland 1990-2000		
Survey year	**England**			**Scotland**			
	11-15 years			12-15 years			
	Boys	Girls	Total	Boys	Girls	Total	
	Percentage who drank alcohol in the past week						
1990	22	20	21	16	12	14	
1992	24	17	21	16	13	14	
1994	25	22	24	21	19	20	
1996	27	26	27	24	21	23	
1998	23	18	21	20	17	19	
2000	25	23	24	21	20	21	
Bases (2000)	*3540*	*3313*	*6853*	*2407*	*2317*	*4724*	

[a] Figures in this table are **not** age-standardised.

Table 14.13

Prevalence of drug use in the last month and the last year, by age and country: 1998–2000[a]

All pupils											England and Scotland 1998-2000
	England						**Scotland**				
	11 years	12 years	13 years	14 years	15 years	**11-15 years**	12 years	13 years	14 years	15 years	**12-15 years**
	Percentage who used drugs										
Used drugs in the past month											
1998	0	2	4	10	18	7	2	8	14	24	10
1999	1	2	5	11	18	7	b	b	b	b	b
2000	3	3	5	13	21	9	1	8	15	22	10
Used drugs in the last year											
1998	1	4	7	16	28	11	3	11	22	35	15
1999	1	4	8	16	29	12	b	b	b	b	b
2000	3	5	9	19	29	14	3	11	22	30	14
Bases (2000)	*1153*	*1385*	*1392*	*1405*	*1520*	*6855*	*1572*	*1172*	*1124*	*807*	*4675*

[a] Figures in this table are **not** age-standardised.

[b] Data were not collected in 1999 in Scotland.

Appendix A: **Survey design**

Sample design

A sample was required of children of secondary school age with separate national samples for England and Scotland. The sample for Scotland is described in the separate survey report for Scotland.

In England the target population was children who were in years 7 to 11 inclusive in secondary schools, or at an equivalent level in middle and upper schools.

The survey covered almost all types of secondary school (comprehensive, secondary modern, grammar and other secondary schools) in both the maintained and non-maintained sectors of education. Only special schools (for children with learning disabilities) and hospital special schools (for children spending a period in hospital) were excluded from the survey.

The sample was selected in two stages. At the first stage 313 schools were selected from the NFER database[1] which was first sorted by type of school (comprehensive, secondary modern, grammar and private), whether schools were single sex or mixed, local education authority and then finally by number of pupils. For each school, the probability of selection was proportional to the numbers of pupils aged 11-15 recorded on DfES Form 7 census data, collected in January 1999. This means that larger schools had a higher chance of inclusion.

At the second stage, approximately 35 pupils were then selected in each school to give an appropriately sized group for conducting the survey in one place during a single lesson. Clearly, at this stage, each pupil in larger schools had a relatively small chance of being selected. This counter balances the method of selecting schools to fulfil the criterion that, overall, every eligible pupil had an equal chance of participating.

All 313 schools were approached, invited to take part,[2] and asked to send an electronic copy of their registers to NFER. For schools that provided a register, a systematic sample of pupils was taken by NFER and details of the selected pupils were passed back to the school and onto interviewers. For schools that were unable or unwilling to provide an electronic copy of registers, interviewers visited the schools to take a manual systematic sample. The 35 or so selected pupils per school were drawn from across all classes in school years 7-11.

Probabilities of selection

Given the requirement that each child in the target population should have the same probability of being selected to take part in the survey, the overall probability of selection (or sampling fraction) is the product of the sampling fractions at the first and second stages, that is:

$$F = f_1 \times f_2$$

where f_1 = probability of selecting the school
f_2 = probability of selecting the pupil

Schools were sampled with probability proportional to the number of pupils aged 11-15, so that roughly equal numbers of pupils could be sampled from each selected school. Thus:

$$f_1 = n_1 \times \frac{s}{S}$$

where n_1 = total number of schools to be selected
          s = number of pupils in an individual school aged 11-15
          S = total number of pupils aged 11-15

and $f_2 = \frac{n_2}{s}$

where n_2 = number of pupils to be selected from each school

Overall, therefore, for each pupil the sampling fraction is:

$$F = (n_1 \times \frac{s}{S}) \times (\frac{n_2}{s}) = \frac{n_1 \times n_2}{S}$$

Sample size

The survey aimed to achieve a sample of about 7500 pupils in England. Based on previous surveys in this series, it was expected that about 80% of schools would co-operate, and that 90% of selected pupils would agree to take part in the survey. On this basis, 313 schools were selected with the aim of selecting an average of 35 pupils per participating school.

As in previous years, schools with fewer than 35 pupils in the required age ranges were deleted from the sampling frame.

Despite prolonged efforts over several months by NFER and the National Centre for Social Research, it did not prove possible to achieve the expected response rate. Among the reasons cited by schools declining to take part were:

- A perceived overload of both local and national surveys covering this topic, leading to an 'overemphasis' on the subject with pupils

- An unwillingness to sacrifice curriculum time for this purpose

- Overload/shortages of school staff time to help in the administration of the survey

Ultimately 225 schools (72%) participated. The mean number of pupils selected randomly was 36, one more than projected. The vast majority of selected pupils participated (87%) yielding a total sample of 7089 pupils.

Stratification of the sampling frame

Previous surveys in the series have shown that children's behaviour varies according to the characteristics of the school rather more than by region, so schools were stratified in England as follows:

1. Into four main school types:
   Comprehensive
   Grammar
   Secondary modern
   Private

3. Within these types by:
   Boys only
   Girls only
   Mixed

4. In each of the 12 major strata formed, schools were ordered by local education authority within region.

Table A1 shows the allocation of the required sample of schools to each of the major strata and the number of schools actually selected in England. **(Table A1)**

Sampling within selected schools

Sampling fractions at the second stage (i.e. within schools) were calculated by NFER and adjusted for the effect of rounding on the number of schools selected in each stratum at the first stage. Expected quota sizes are shown in Table A2. These were based on information about the number of pupils at each school collected in the DfES's annual school census of January 1999. Actual quota sizes therefore varied to the extent to which the size of the school had changed in the interim. **(Table A2)**

Precision of results and the measurement of change

Since the data in this report were obtained from a sample of the population, they are subject to sampling error. Any sample is only one of an almost infinite number that might have been selected, all producing slightly different estimates. Sampling error stems from the probability that any selected sample is not completely representative of the population from which it is drawn.

Sampling error shows the amount by which the value of a sample estimate of a variable can be expected to differ from the true value of that variable in the population. With a simple random sample, the formula for calculating the sampling error for a percentage p, is:

$$\sqrt{\frac{p(100-p)}{n}}$$

where n is the sample size

Since the sample of pupils was clustered in schools, sampling errors are not the same as they would have been for a simple random sample of the same size. Sampling errors for four key variables which take account of the complex design are shown in Tables A3-A6 in this appendix.

The formula for calculating sampling errors of differences in percentages p_1 and p_2 between surveys (assuming simple random samples) is:

$$\sqrt{\frac{p_1(100-p_1)}{n_1} + \frac{p_2(100-p_2)}{n_1}}$$

In general, attention is drawn to differences between estimates only when they are significant at the 0.05 confidence level, thus indicating that there is less than 5% probability that the observed difference could be due to random sampling variation, when no difference occurred in the population from which the sample is drawn.

It is important to recognise that sampling error is only one of the sources of error which affect the accuracy of any survey results. Other sources of inaccuracy include non-response bias, and over-and under-reporting, both of which are difficult to quantify. It can be assumed, however, that since the results compared in this report are from surveys conducted in the same way and using the same methods of collecting information, non-sampling errors will be similar in each survey and so will not affect comparisons.

Sampling errors

Tables A3-A6 give true standard errors and 95% confidence intervals, taking account of the complex sample design for four key variables. Since the survey used a multi-stage sample design which involved both clustering and stratification it would be incorrect to calculate standard errors using the formulae which assumes a simple random sample design. The calculation of the standard errors and design effects (defts) was carried out using Kish's methodology.[3] **(Tables A3-A6)**

Fieldwork Procedures

Schools were given letters for pupils to take home and give to their parents or guardians informing them of the survey. Parents were asked to reply only if they did not want their child to take part in the survey.[4]

Interviewers arranged with schools a convenient time to conduct the survey. If four or more pupils were absent on this occasion, interviewers organised one further visit to the school so that these pupils had a second opportunity to take part.

All pupils taking part in the survey gathered together in a classroom for one school period to complete a questionnaire and a 7 day retrospective smoking diary under the supervision of an interviewer. The interviewer gave a brief introduction explaining why the survey was being carried out, and explained how the questionnaire and diary should be filled in. The questionnaire and smoking diary used are contained in the Appendices C and D.

Pupils were not allowed to discuss the questions with each other or look at other pupils' answers. Thus 'exam-like' conditions were sought, though pupils could request and receive help if they did not understand questions. In general, teachers were not present during the completion of questionnaires in order to encourage pupils to give honest answers.

Interviewers stressed that pupils' answers would be completely confidential and that their answers would not reflect on them or their school. Questionnaires were serial numbered for administrative purposes, but serial numbers were not linked to pupils' names.

Non-response weighting

A logistic regression of school level response was undertaken, in which school level variables associated with a differential response were entered as independent variables. A high percentage of pupils attaining 5 or more A*-C GSCEs was most powerful predictor of non-response. No other factors were significant predictors once GCSE pass rates were taken into account.

A non-response weight was calculated using the logistic regression model, and key estimates were compared with and without this non-response weight applied to the data. These key estimates were prevalence of cigarette smoking, prevalence of drinking in the last week and use of drugs in the last month, last year or ever. Comparisons were made for different ages and both sexes. There were no significant differences between the weighted and unweighted estimates, even at the 50% confidence level. Therefore the data in this report are not weighted and are comparable with all other surveys in the series.

Notes and references

1 NFER maintains a database containing records for all schools in England, Northern Ireland, Scotland and Wales. It also contains schools in the Isle of Man, the Channel Islands, Service Children's Education Authority (armed forces) schools and British schools around the world. In addition, details are held for all colleges in the Further and Higher Education sectors and for all Universities.

2 One school was deemed ineligible after being approached, as it was a Japanese language school.

3 Kish, L. (1970) Survey Sampling, London: John Wiley.

4 Two schools who had sent their own letters out asking parents to reply to give permission for their child to take part had to be excluded from the survey, because of the potential response bias.

Allocation of primary sampling units (PSUs) to strata

England 2000

Type of school	Population[a]	Estimated PSUs	Actual PSUs[b]
Comprehensive			
Boys	85,239	9.01	9
Girls	122,126	12.94	13
Mixed	2,360,649	249.57	249
Grammar			
Boys	36,706	3.88	4
Girls	39,418	4.17	5
Mixed	28,136	2.97	2
Secondary modern			
Boys	8,797	0.93	2
Girls	11,822	1.25	1
Mixed	64,928	6.87	7
Private			
Boys	44,156	4.66	3
Girls	60,476	6.39	8
Mixed	97,836	10.34	10
Total	**2,960,601**	**312.98**	**313**

[a] DfEE (now DfES) Form 7 census data, collected January 1999.

[b] Small strata have been combined in order to improve the efficiency of the sampling, so expected and actual PSUs may differ.

Quota sizes and maximum sample sizes expected, by school type

England 2000

Type of school	Sampled schools	Quota size	Maximum expected sample of pupils
Comprehensive			
Boys	9	35	315
Girls	13	35	455
Mixed	249	35	8,715
Grammar			
Boys	4	35	140
Girls	5	35	175
Mixed	2	35	70
Secondary modern			
Boys	2	35	70
Girls	1	35	35
Mixed	7	35	245
Private			
Boys	3	35	105
Girls	8	35	280
Mixed	10	35	350
Total	**313**		**10,955**

True standard errors and 95% Confidence Intervals for the prevalence of smoking, by sex and age

England 2000

	Sample size	(p)	True standard error of p	95% Confidence Interval		
				Lower	Upper	Deft
Boys						
Age 11	623	2.6%	0.6%	1.4%	3.8%	0.95
Age 12	749	4.0%	0.7%	2.5%	5.5%	1.08
Age 13	737	11.0%	1.1%	8.7%	13.3%	0.99
Age 14	752	16.8%	1.4%	14.1%	19.5%	1.02
Age 15	794	28.1%	1.7%	24.8%	31.4%	1.13
Total	**3655**	**13.0%**	**0.6%**	**11.8%**	**14.2%**	**1.17**
Girls						
Age 11	574	1.6%	0.5%	0.6%	2.6%	1.03
Age 12	687	6.3%	0.9%	4.4%	8.2%	1.04
Age 13	697	18.7%	1.5%	15.8%	21.6%	1.00
Age 14	688	28.2%	1.7%	24.8%	31.6%	1.01
Age 15	765	38.0%	1.8%	34.4%	41.6%	1.07
Total	**3411**	**19.6%**	**0.7%**	**18.1%**	**21.1%**	**1.20**
Total						
Age 11	1197	2.1%	0.4%	1.3%	2.9%	1.05
Age 12	1436	5.1%	0.6%	3.9%	6.3%	1.19
Age 13	1434	14.7%	1.0%	12.8%	16.6%	1.05
Age 14	1440	22.2%	1.1%	20.0%	24.4%	1.07
Age 15	1559	33.0%	1.3%	30.5%	35.5%	1.14
Total	**7066**	**16.2%**	**0.5%**	**15.2%**	**17.2%**	**1.30**

True standard errors and 95% Confidence Intervals for the proportion who drink at least once a week, by sex and age

England 2000

	Sample size	(p)	True standard error of p	95% Confidence Interval		
				Lower	Upper	Deft
Boys						
Age 11	621	3.5%	0.8%	2.0%	5.0%	1.08
Age 12	752	5.6%	0.9%	3.8%	7.4%	1.17
Age 13	740	15.1%	1.3%	12.5%	17.7%	1.02
Age 14	752	25.7%	1.6%	22.6%	28.8%	1.01
Age 15	796	42.6%	1.9%	38.8%	46.4%	1.20
Total	**3661**	**19.3%**	**0.7%**	**17.9%**	**20.7%**	**1.19**
Girls						
Age 11	573	2.4%	0.6%	1.1%	3.7%	1.00
Age 12	685	3.8%	0.8%	2.3%	5.3%	1.06
Age 13	696	12.8%	1.3%	10.3%	15.3%	1.01
Age 14	689	21.9%	1.5%	18.9%	24.9%	0.97
Age 15	764	38.1%	1.8%	34.5%	41.7%	1.08
Total	**3407**	**16.8%**	**0.7%**	**15.5%**	**18.1%**	**1.14**
Total						
Age 11	1194	3.0%	0.5%	2.0%	4.0%	1.05
Age 12	1437	4.7%	0.6%	3.5%	5.9%	1.14
Age 13	1436	14.0%	0.9%	12.2%	15.8%	1.01
Age 14	1441	23.9%	1.1%	21.7%	26.1%	0.98
Age 15	1560	40.4%	1.3%	37.8%	43.0%	1.17
Total	**7068**	**18.1%**	**0.5%**	**17.1%**	**19.1%**	**1.30**

Table A5

True standard errors and 95% Confidence Intervals for mean alcohol consumption last week, by sex and age

England 2000

	Sample size	Mean units	True standard error of mean	95% Confidence Interval		Deft
				Lower	Upper	
Boys						
Age 11	602	0.39	0.19	0.01	0.78	1.00
Age 12	712	0.42	0.10	0.22	0.61	1.09
Age 13	690	1.42	0.42	0.59	2.24	1.14
Age 14	697	3.02	0.34	2.35	3.68	1.16
Age 15	734	7.56	0.58	6.42	8.71	1.02
Total	**3435**	**2.67**	**0.18**	**2.31**	**3.03**	**1.15**
Girls						
Age 11	558	0.09	0.04	0.02	0.16	1.03
Age 12	670	0.31	0.07	0.18	0.44	0.90
Age 13	669	0.92	0.15	0.63	1.21	1.06
Age 14	664	2.94	0.33	2.30	3.58	1.04
Age 15	731	5.20	0.38	4.46	5.95	1.00
Total	**3292**	**2.02**	**0.13**	**1.76**	**2.27**	**1.13**
Total						
Age 11	1160	0.25	0.10	0.05	0.45	1.01
Age 12	1382	0.37	0.06	0.25	0.48	1.00
Age 13	1359	1.17	0.22	0.74	1.60	1.10
Age 14	1361	2.98	0.24	2.50	3.46	1.13
Age 15	1465	6.39	0.36	5.68	7.09	1.09
Total	**6727**	**2.35**	**0.12**	**2.11**	**2.59**	**1.30**

Table A6

True standard errors and 95% Confidence Intervals for the proportion who have ever used drugs, by sex and age

England 2000

	Sample size	(p)	True standard error of p	95% Confidence Interval		Deft
				Lower	Upper	
Boys						
Age 11	597	5.7%	1.0%	3.8%	7.6%	1.05
Age 12	731	6.6%	0.9%	4.8%	8.4%	1.04
Age 13	717	12.6%	1.3%	10.1%	15.1%	1.08
Age 14	731	23.5%	1.6%	20.4%	26.6%	1.02
Age 15	773	34.5%	1.7%	31.1%	37.9%	1.03
Total	**3549**	**17.2%**	**0.7%**	**15.9%**	**18.5%**	**1.06**
Girls						
Age 11	556	3.6%	0.8%	2.1%	5.1%	1.00
Age 12	660	6.2%	0.9%	4.4%	8.0%	1.01
Age 13	678	12.1%	1.2%	9.7%	14.5%	0.97
Age 14	676	21.3%	1.6%	18.1%	24.5%	1.07
Age 15	749	30.2%	1.8%	26.6%	33.8%	1.17
Total	**3319**	**15.5%**	**0.7%**	**14.2%**	**16.8%**	**1.19**
Total						
Age 11	1153	4.7%	0.6%	3.5%	5.9%	0.89
Age 12	1391	6.4%	0.7%	5.1%	7.7%	1.07
Age 13	1395	12.3%	0.9%	10.5%	14.1%	1.06
Age 14	1407	22.5%	1.1%	20.3%	24.7%	1.05
Age 15	1522	32.4%	1.3%	29.8%	35.0%	1.19
Total	**6868**	**16.4%**	**0.5%**	**15.4%**	**17.4%**	**1.23**

Appendix B: **Analysis techniques**

In addition to extensive two-way and three-way cross-tabulations of data, this report includes analyses which made use of the statistical techniques outlined here.

Age standardisation

Age is a key factor in both attitudes and behaviour related to smoking, drinking and drug use and most of the survey estimates show significant differences between pupils of different ages. When different subgroups' answers to particular questions are being compared, it is necessary to consider the potential effect of the age profiles of these subgroups. If the age-profiles differ substantially, then this may account for all or part of any differences observed on the measures concerned.

Age standardisation is a technique which is used to weight the data so that the age-profiles of different subgroups become the same (are standardised). Thus one is able to establish whether or not attitudinal or behavioural differences found between subgroups are due solely to the ages of pupils in different subgroups.

Logistic regression

Logistic regression is used to investigate the effect of two or more independent or predictor variables on a two-category (binary) outcome variable. The parameter estimates from a logistic regression model for each independent variable give an estimate of the effect of that variable on the outcome variable, adjusted for all other independent variables in the model.

Logistic regression models the logarithm of the 'odds' of a binary outcome variable. The 'odds' of an outcome is the ratio of the probability of its occurring to the probability of its not occurring. The parameter estimates obtained from logistic regression have been presented as odds ratios for ease of interpretation. The odds ratios for a given category of a categorical independent variable gives the change in the odds of the outcome occurring compared to the overall odds ('to average'). In logistic regression a 95% confidence interval which does not include 1.0 indicates that the given parameter estimate is statistically significant.

Multi-level modelling

Multi-level modelling is used to examine whether the characteristics of schools taking part impact on pupils' behaviours, over and above any effects due to the individual characteristics of the pupils.

The benefit of using a multi-level modelling approach over traditional multiple regression is that, whilst either will give unbiased estimates of regression coefficients, only multi-level models give accurate estimates of the standard errors of these coefficients (because the models account for the correlations within schools). This is important when assessing the relative impact of school characteristics on the survey's key estimates.

Appendix C: **Questionnaire**

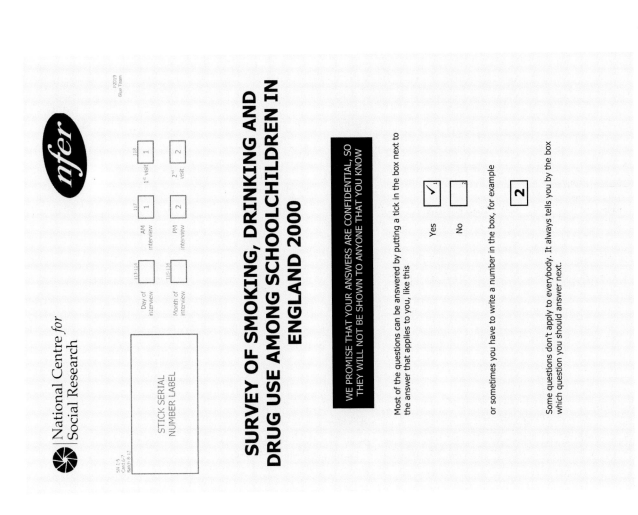

National Centre *for* Social Research

nfer

P2019
Blue Team

SN 1-5
Card 6-7
Batch 8-12

STICK SERIAL
NUMBER LABEL

Day of interview — 113-114

Month of interview — 115-116

AM interview — 117 — 1

PM interview — 2

1st visit — 118 — 1

2nd visit — 2

SURVEY OF SMOKING, DRINKING AND DRUG USE AMONG SCHOOLCHILDREN IN ENGLAND 2000

WE PROMISE THAT YOUR ANSWERS ARE CONFIDENTIAL, SO THEY WILL NOT BE SHOWN TO ANYONE THAT YOU KNOW

Most of the questions can be answered by putting a tick in the box next to the answer that applies to you, like this

Yes ✓₁

No ☐₂

or sometimes you have to write a number in the box, for example

2

Some questions don't apply to everybody. It always tells you by the box which question you should answer next.

Q 1 Are you a boy or a girl?

Boy ☐ 1
Girl ☐ 2 → **Go to Question 2**

119

Q 2 Which year are you in at school?

Year 7 ☐ 1
Year 8 ☐ 2
Year 9 ☐ 3
Year 10 ☐ 4
Year 11 ☐ 5 → **Go to Question 3**

120

Q 3 How old are you now?

10 years old ☐ 01
11 years old ☐ 02
12 years old ☐ 03
13 years old ☐ 04
14 years old ☐ 05
15 years old ☐ 06
16 years old ☐ 07
17 years old ☐ 08 → **Go to Question 4**

121-122

Q 4 When is your birthday?

Date.............
Month.............
→ **Go to Question 5**

DO NOT WRITE IN THIS BOX
D 123-124
M 125-126

page 1

Q 5 To which of these ethnic groups do you belong?

White ☐ 1
Mixed ☐ 2
Asian or Asian British ☐ 3
Black or Black British ☐ 4
Chinese ☐ 5
Other ☐ 6 → **Go to Question 6**

127

The next set of questions are about cigarettes. Remember that your name is not on the questionnaire, so no-one who knows you will find out your answers.

Q 6 Do you smoke cigarettes at all nowadays?

Yes ☐ 1 → **Go to Question 7**
No ☐ 2

128

Q 7 Now read all the following statements carefully and tick the box next to the one which best describes you.

I have never smoked ☐ 1 → **Go to Question 8**
I have only ever tried smoking once ☐ 2 → **Go to Question 9**
I used to smoke sometimes but I never smoke a cigarette now ☐ 3
I sometimes smoke cigarettes now but I don't smoke as many as one a week ☐ 4 → **Go to Question 15**
I usually smoke between one and six cigarettes a week ☐ 5
I usually smoke more than six cigarettes a week ☐ 6 → **Go to Question 10**

129

Q 8 Just to check, read the statements below carefully and tick the box next to the one which best describes you.

I have never tried smoking a cigarette, not even a puff or two ☐ 1 → **Go to Question 9**
I did once have a puff or two of a cigarette, but I never smoke now ☐ 2
I do sometimes smoke cigarettes ☐ 3 → **Go to Question 15**

130

page 2

Q 9 How do you think your family would feel if you started smoking?

- They would stop me
- They would try to persuade me not to smoke
- They would do nothing
- They would encourage me to smoke
- I don't know

Go to Question 20 on page 6

Q 10 How long is it since you started smoking at least one cigarette a week?

- Less than 3 months
- 3-6 months
- 6 months to 1 year
- more than 1 year

Go to Question 11

Q 11 How easy or difficult would you find it to go without smoking for as long as a week?

- Very difficult
- Fairly difficult
- Fairly easy
- Very easy

Go to Question 12

Q 12 How easy or difficult would you find it to give up smoking altogether if you wanted to?

- Very difficult
- Fairly difficult
- Fairly easy
- Very easy

Go to Question 13

Q 13 Would you like to give up smoking altogether?

- Yes
- No
- I don't know

Go to Question 14

Q 14 Have you ever tried to give up smoking?

- Yes
- No

Go to Question 15

Q 15 How does your family feel about you smoking?

- They stop me
- They try to persuade me not to smoke
- They do nothing
- They encourage me to smoke
- They don't know I smoke → **Go to Question 16**
- I don't know → **Go to Question 17**

Q 16 How do you think your family would feel if they knew that you smoked?

- They would stop me
- They would try to persuade me not to smoke
- They would do nothing
- They would encourage me to smoke
- I don't know

Go to Question 17

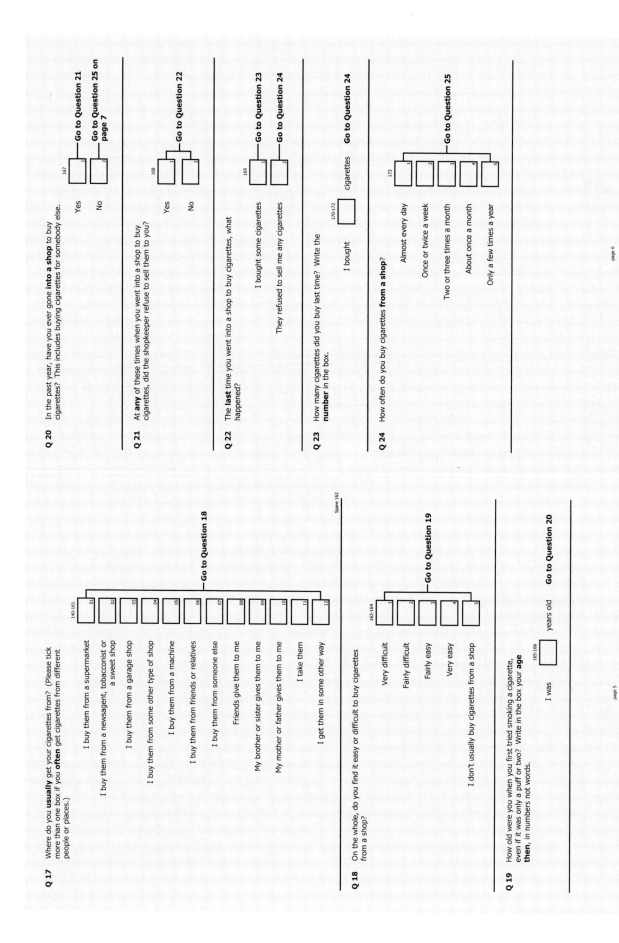

Q 17 Where do you **usually** get your cigarettes from? (Please tick more than one box if you **often** get cigarettes from different people or places.)

- I buy them from a supermarket
- I buy them from a newsagent, tobacconist or a sweet shop
- I buy them from a garage shop
- I buy them from some other type of shop
- I buy them from a machine
- I buy them from friends or relatives
- I buy them from someone else
- Friends give them to me
- My brother or sister gives them to me
- My mother or father gives them to me
- I take them
- I get them in some other way

Go to Question 18

Q 18 On the whole, do you find it easy or difficult to buy cigarettes from a shop?

- Very difficult
- Fairly difficult
- Fairly easy
- Very easy
- I don't usually buy cigarettes from a shop

Go to Question 19

Q 19 How old were you when you first tried smoking a cigarette, even if it was only a puff or two? Write in the box your **age then**, in numbers not words.

I was [ ] years old **Go to Question 20**

page 5

Q 20 In the past year, have you ever gone **into a shop** to buy cigarettes? This includes buying cigarettes for somebody else.

- Yes → **Go to Question 21**
- No → **Go to Question 25 on page 7**

Q 21 At **any** of these times when you went into a shop to buy cigarettes, did the shopkeeper refuse to sell them to you?

- Yes → **Go to Question 22**
- No → **Go to Question 24**

Q 22 The **last** time you went into a shop to buy cigarettes, what happened?

- I bought some cigarettes → **Go to Question 23**
- They refused to sell me any cigarettes → **Go to Question 24**

Q 23 How many cigarettes did you buy last time? Write the **number** in the box.

I bought [ ] cigarettes **Go to Question 24**

Q 24 How often do you buy cigarettes **from a shop**?

- Almost every day
- Once or twice a week
- Two or three times a month
- About once a month
- Only a few times a year

Go to Question 25

page 6

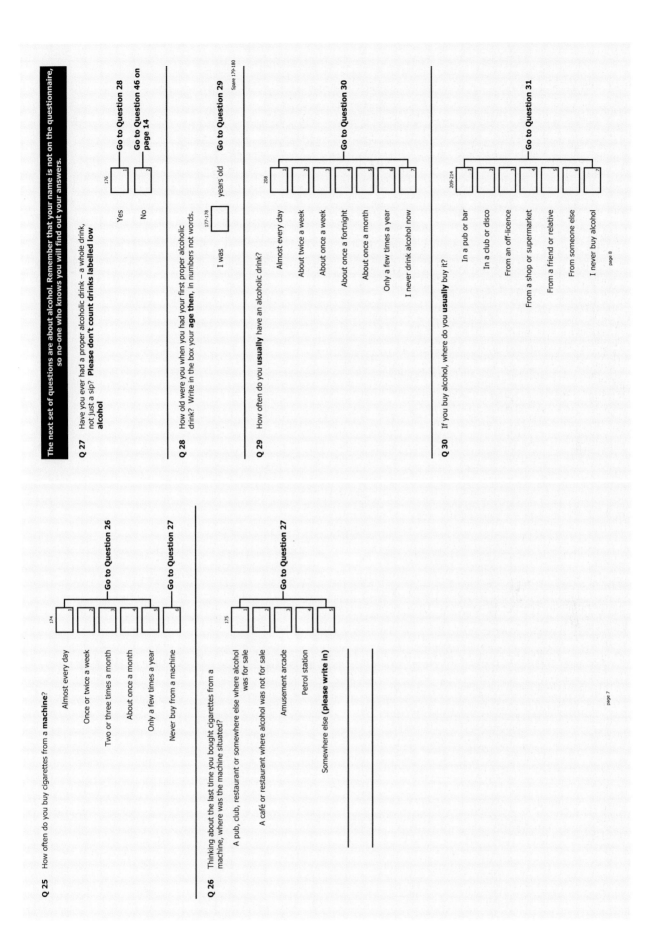

Q 25 How often do you buy cigarettes from a **machine**?

- Almost every day (1)
- Once or twice a week (2)
- Two or three times a month (3)
- About once a month (4)
- Only a few times a year (5) — **Go to Question 26**
- Never buy from a machine (6) — **Go to Question 27**

174

Q 26 Thinking about the last time you bought cigarettes from a machine, where was the machine situated?

- A pub, club, restaurant or somewhere else where alcohol was for sale (1)
- A café or restaurant where alcohol was not for sale (2)
- Amusement arcade (3)
- Petrol station (4)
- Somewhere else **(please write in)** (5)

— **Go to Question 27**

175

The next set of questions are about alcohol. Remember that your name is not on the questionnaire, so no-one who knows you will find out your answers.

Q 27 Have you ever had a proper alcoholic drink, not just a sip? **Please don't count drinks labelled low alcohol**

- Yes (1) — **Go to Question 28**
- No (2) — **Go to Question 46 on page 14**

176

Q 28 How old were you when you had your first proper alcoholic drink? Write in the box your **age then**, in numbers not words.

I was [ ] years old — **Go to Question 29**

177-178

Spare 179-180

Q 29 How often do you **usually** have an alcoholic drink?

- Almost every day (1)
- About twice a week (2)
- About once a week (3)
- About once a fortnight (4)
- About once a month (5)
- Only a few times a year (6)
- I never drink alcohol now (7)

— **Go to Question 30**

208

Q 30 If you buy alcohol, where do you **usually** buy it?

- In a pub or bar (1)
- In a club or disco (2)
- From an off-licence (3)
- From a shop or supermarket (4)
- From a friend or relative (5)
- From someone else (6)
- I never buy alcohol (7)

— **Go to Question 31**

209-214

page 7

page 8

Q 31 When did you **last** have an alcoholic drink?

215

Today ☐1 **Go to Question 32**

Yesterday ☐2

Some other time during the last 7 days ☐3

1 week, but less than 2 weeks ago ☐4 **Go to Question 46 on page 14**

2 weeks, but less than 4 weeks ago ☐5

1 month, but less than 6 months ago ☐6

6 months ago or more ☐7

Q 32 On which of these days during **the last 7 days** did you have an alcoholic drink? **Tick whichever apply**

216-222

Sunday ☐1 **Go to Question 33**

Monday ☐2

Tueday ☐3

Wednesday ☐4

Thursday ☐5

Friday ☐6

Saturday ☐7

Q 33 During the **last 7 days**, how much BEER, LAGER AND CIDER have you drunk? Please don't count drinks labelled low alcohol.

223

Have not drunk beer, lager or cider in the last 7 days ☐1 **Go to Question 36**

Less than half a pint ☐2

Half a pint or more ☐3 **Go to Question 34**

Q 34 Write in the boxes below the number of pints, half pints, large cans, small cans and bottles of BEER, LAGER AND CIDER drunk in the last 7 days.

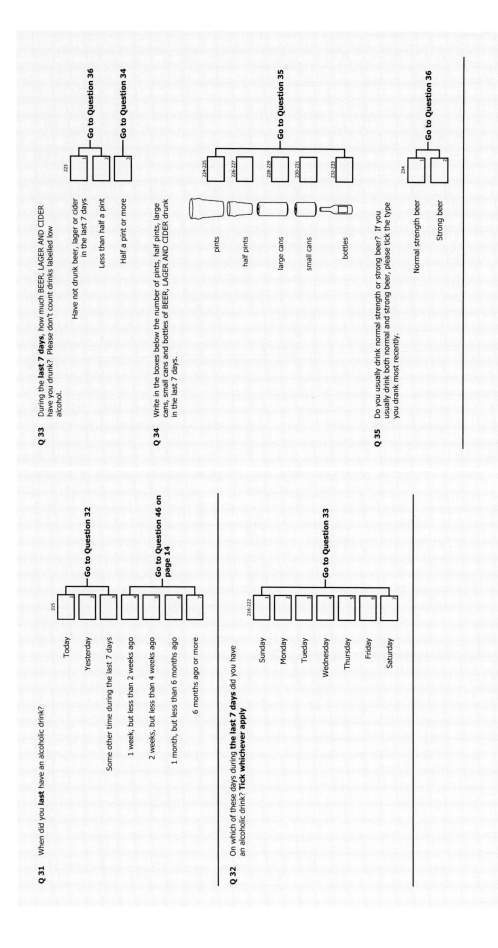

pints 224-225

half pints 226-227

large cans 228-229 **Go to Question 35**

small cans 230-231

bottles 232-233

Q 35 Do you usually drink normal strength or strong beer? If you usually drink both normal and strong beer, please tick the type you drank most recently.

234

Normal strength beer ☐1 **Go to Question 36**

Strong beer ☐2

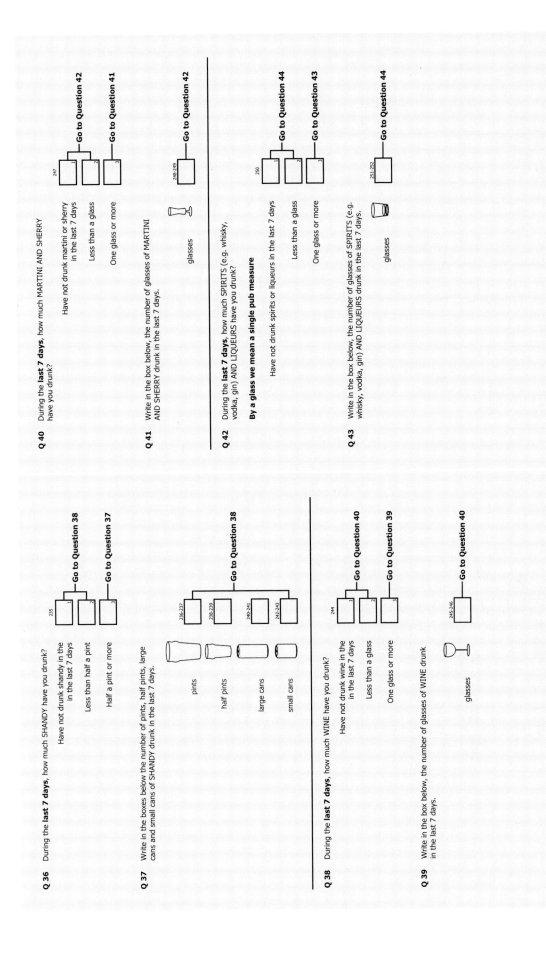

Q 36 During the **last 7 days**, how much SHANDY have you drunk?

Have not drunk shandy in the in the last 7 days → **Go to Question 38**

Less than half a pint

Half a pint or more → **Go to Question 37**

235

Q 37 Write in the boxes below the number of pints, half pints, large cans and small cans of SHANDY drunk in the last 7 days.

pints — 236-237

half pints — 238-239

large cans — 240-241

small cans — 242-243

→ **Go to Question 38**

Q 38 During the **last 7 days**, how much WINE have you drunk?

Have not drunk wine in the in the last 7 days → **Go to Question 40**

Less than a glass

One glass or more → **Go to Question 39**

244

Q 39 Write in the box below, the number of glasses of WINE drunk in the last 7 days.

glasses — 245-246

→ **Go to Question 40**

page 11

Q 40 During the **last 7 days**, how much MARTINI AND SHERRY have you drunk?

Have not drunk martini or sherry in the last 7 days → **Go to Question 42**

Less than a glass

One glass or more → **Go to Question 41**

247

Q 41 Write in the box below, the number of glasses of MARTINI AND SHERRY drunk in the last 7 days.

glasses — 248-249

→ **Go to Question 42**

Q 42 During the **last 7 days**, how much SPIRITS (e.g. whisky, vodka, gin) AND LIQUEURS have you drunk?

By a glass we mean a single pub measure

Have not drunk spirits or liqueurs in the last 7 days → **Go to Question 44**

Less than a glass

One glass or more → **Go to Question 43**

250

Q 43 Write in the box below, the number of glasses of SPIRITS (e.g. whisky, vodka, gin) AND LIQUEURS drunk in the last 7 days.

glasses — 251-252

→ **Go to Question 44**

page 12

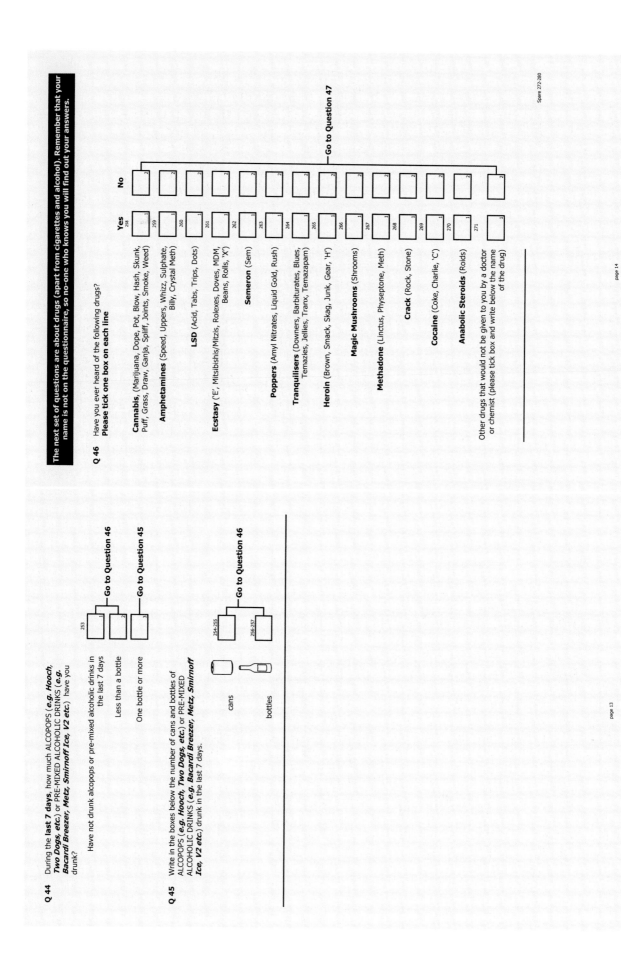

Q 44 During the **last 7 days**, how much ALCOPOPS (*e.g. Hooch, Two Dogs, etc.*) or PRE-MIXED ALCOHOLIC DRINKS (*e.g. Bacardi Breezer, Metz, Smirnoff Ice, V2 etc.*) have you drunk?

Have not drunk alcopops or pre-mixed alcoholic drinks in the last 7 days — 1 → **Go to Question 46**

Less than a bottle — 2

One bottle or more — 3 → **Go to Question 45**

253

Q 45 Write in the boxes below the number of cans and bottles of ALCOPOPS (*e.g. Hooch, Two Dogs, etc.*) or PRE-MIXED ALCOHOLIC DRINKS (*e.g. Bacardi Breezer, Metz, Smirnoff Ice, V2 etc.*) drunk in the last 7 days.

cans — 254-255 → **Go to Question 46**

bottles — 256-257

page 13

The next set of questions are about drugs (apart from cigarettes and alcohol). Remember that your name is not on the questionnaire, so no-one who knows you will find out your answers.

Q 46 Have you ever heard of the following drugs?
Please tick one box on each line

	Yes	No
Cannabis, (Marijuana, Dope, Pot, Blow, Hash, Skunk, Puff, Grass, Draw, Ganja, Spliff, Joints, Smoke, Weed)	258 ☐1	☐2
Amphetamines (Speed, Uppers, Whizz, Sulphate, Billy, Crystal Meth)	259 ☐1	☐2
LSD (Acid, Tabs, Trips, Dots)	260 ☐1	☐2
Ecstasy ('E', Mitsibishis/Mitzis, Rolexes, Doves, MDM, Beans, Rolls, 'X')	261 ☐1	☐2
Semeron (Sem)	262 ☐1	☐2
Poppers (Amyl Nitrates, Liquid Gold, Rush)	263 ☐1	☐2
Tranquilisers (Downers, Barbiturates, Blues, Temazies, Jellies, Tranx, Temazapam)	264 ☐1	☐2
Heroin (Brown, Smack, Skag, Junk, Gear, 'H')	265 ☐1	☐2
Magic Mushrooms (Shrooms)	266 ☐1	☐2
Methadone (Linctus, Physeptone, Meth)	267 ☐1	☐2
Crack (Rock, Stone)	268 ☐1	☐2
Cocaine (Coke, Charlie, 'C')	269 ☐1	☐2
Anabolic Steroids (Roids)	270 ☐1	☐2
Other drugs that would not be given to you by a doctor or chemist (please tick box and write below the name of the drug)	271 ☐1	☐2

→ **Go to Question 47**

Spare 272-280

page 14

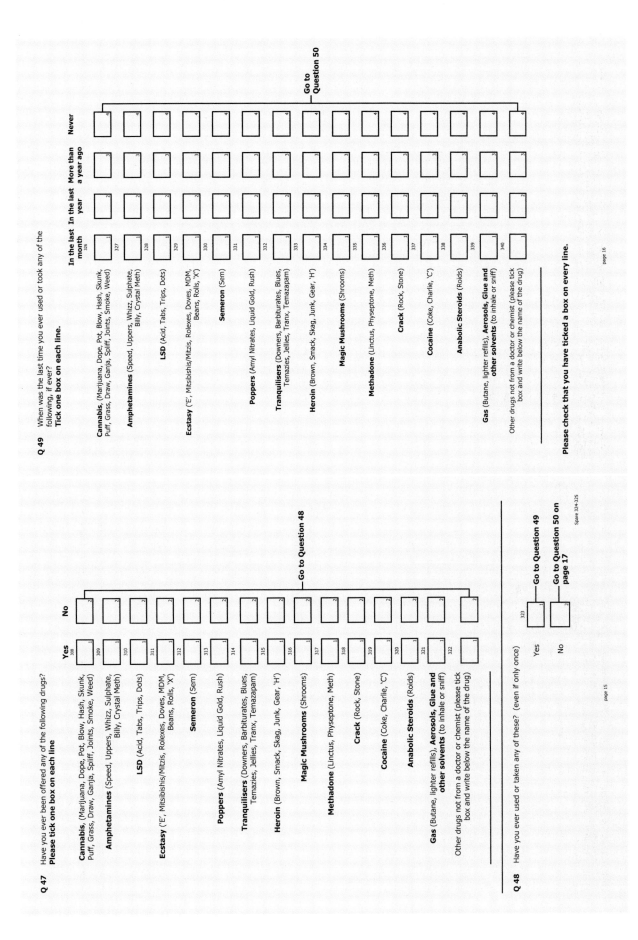

Q 47 Have you ever been offered any of the following drugs?
Please tick one box on each line

Yes / No

- **Cannabis,** (Marijuana, Dope, Pot, Blow, Hash, Skunk, Puff, Grass, Draw, Ganja, Spliff, Joints, Smoke, Weed)
- **Amphetamines** (Speed, Uppers, Whizz, Sulphate, Billy, Crystal Meth)
- **LSD** (Acid, Tabs, Trips, Dots)
- **Ecstasy** ('E', Mitsibishis/Mitzis, Rolexes, Doves, MDM, Beans, Rolls, 'X')
- **Semeron** (Sem)
- **Poppers** (Amyl Nitrates, Liquid Gold, Rush)
- **Tranquilisers** (Downers, Barbiturates, Blues, Temazies, Jellies, Tranx, Temazapam)
- **Heroin** (Brown, Smack, Skag, Junk, Gear, 'H')
- **Magic Mushrooms** (Shrooms)
- **Methadone** (Linctus, Physeptone, Meth)
- **Crack** (Rock, Stone)
- **Cocaine** (Coke, Charlie, 'C')
- **Anabolic Steroids** (Roids)
- **Gas** (Butane, lighter refills), **Aerosols, Glue and other solvents** (to inhale or sniff)
- Other drugs not from a doctor or chemist (please tick box and write below the name of the drug)

Go to Question 48

Q 48 Have you ever used or taken any of these? (even if only once)

Yes — Go to Question 49
No — Go to Question 50 on page 17

Spare 324-325

Q 49 When was the last time you ever used or took any of the following, if ever?
Tick one box on each line.

In the last month / In the last year / More than a year ago / Never

- **Cannabis,** (Marijuana, Dope, Pot, Blow, Hash, Skunk, Puff, Grass, Draw, Ganja, Spliff, Joints, Smoke, Weed)
- **Amphetamines** (Speed, Uppers, Whizz, Sulphate, Billy, Crystal Meth)
- **LSD** (Acid, Tabs, Trips, Dots)
- **Ecstasy** ('E', Mitsibishis/Mitzis, Rolexes, Doves, MDM, Beans, Rolls, 'X')
- **Semeron** (Sem)
- **Poppers** (Amyl Nitrates, Liquid Gold, Rush)
- **Tranquilisers** (Downers, Barbiturates, Blues, Temazies, Jellies, Tranx, Temazapam)
- **Heroin** (Brown, Smack, Skag, Junk, Gear, 'H')
- **Magic Mushrooms** (Shrooms)
- **Methadone** (Linctus, Physeptone, Meth)
- **Crack** (Rock, Stone)
- **Cocaine** (Coke, Charlie, 'C')
- **Anabolic Steroids** (Roids)
- **Gas** (Butane, lighter refills), **Aerosols, Glue and other solvents** (to inhale or sniff)
- Other drugs not from a doctor or chemist (please tick box and write below the name of the drug)

Never — Go to Question 50

Please check that you have ticked a box on every line.

page 15

page 16

Q 54 In the last twelve months have you had any lessons, videos or discussions in class on the following topics:
Tick one box on each line

	Yes	No	Don't know
Smoking?	346 ☐1	☐2	☐3
Alcohol?	347 ☐1	☐2	☐3
Heroin?	348 ☐1	☐2	☐3
Crack or Cocaine?	349 ☐1	☐2	☐3
Solvent abuse/glue sniffing?	350 ☐1	☐2	☐3
Ecstasy?	351 ☐1	☐2	☐3
Drugs in general?	352 ☐1	☐2	☐3

Go to Question 55

Q 55 Were there any questions you meant to go back and complete? Please check.

If you have finished, please complete the diary next, starting with yesterday and working backwards through the week.

page 18

The next set of questions are more general questions. Remember that your name is not on the questionnaire, so no-one who knows you will find out your answers.

Q 50 Do you get free school meals, or vouchers for free school meals?

341
Yes ☐1
No ☐2 — Go to Question 51
Don't know ☐3

Q 51 Have you ever stayed away from school without permission (truanted)?

342
Yes ☐1
No ☐2 — Go to Question 52
Don't know ☐3

Q 52 Have you ever been excluded from school?

343
Yes ☐1 — Go to Question 53
No ☐2 — Go to Question 54
Don't know ☐3

Q 53 Was it a fixed term exclusion or a permanent exclusion?

A **fixed term exclusion (or suspension)** is when you are not allowed to go to school for a set amount of time because of your behaviour

A **permanent exclusion** is when you are **never** allowed to go back to your school because of your behaviour.

344-345
Fixed-term ☐1
Permanent ☐2 — Go to Question 54
Don't know ☐3

page 17

Appendix D: **Diary**

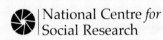

National Centre *for* Social Research

P2019
Blue Team

STICK SERIAL
NUMBER LABEL

SURVEY OF SMOKING, DRINKING AND DRUG USE AMONG SCHOOLCHILDREN 2000

WE PROMISE THAT YOUR ANSWERS ARE CONFIDENTIAL, SO
THEY WILL NOT BE SHOWN TO ANYONE THAT YOU KNOW

WEEKLY DIARY

MONDAY

For each part of the day: **1** Answer the question about what you did by ticking **Yes** or **No**. and **2** If you did not smoke during that part of the day write 0 in the box.

If you smoked during that part of the day write in the box the number of cigarettes you smoked yourself.

		Tick one box		Number of cigarettes smoked	
		Yes (1) / No (2)			
Early morning	Did you get up and go to school?	☐ ☐	→	I smoked ☐ cigarettes	408-409
Morning	Were you at school all morning?	☐ ☐	→	I smoked ☐ cigarettes	410-411
Dinner Time	Did you stay on the school premises all dinnertime?	☐ ☐	→	I smoked ☐ cigarettes	412-413
Afternoon	Were you at school all afternoon?	☐ ☐	→	I smoked ☐ cigarettes	414-415
Tea Time	Did you have your tea at home?	☐ ☐	→	I smoked ☐ cigarettes	416-417
Evening	Did you stay at home all evening?	☐ ☐	→	I smoked ☐ cigarettes	418-419

TUESDAY

For each part of the day: **1** Answer the question about what you did by ticking **Yes** or **No**. and **2** If you did not smoke during that part of the day write 0 in the box.

If you smoked during that part of the day write in the box the number of cigarettes you smoked yourself.

		Tick one box		Number of cigarettes smoked	
		Yes (1) / No (2)			
Early morning	Did you get up and go to school?	☐ ☐	→	I smoked ☐ cigarettes	420-421
Morning	Were you at school all morning?	☐ ☐	→	I smoked ☐ cigarettes	422-423
Dinner Time	Did you stay on the school premises all dinnertime?	☐ ☐	→	I smoked ☐ cigarettes	424-425
Afternoon	Were you at school all afternoon?	☐ ☐	→	I smoked ☐ cigarettes	426-427
Tea Time	Did you have your tea at home?	☐ ☐	→	I smoked ☐ cigarettes	428-429
Evening	Did you stay at home all evening?	☐ ☐	→	I smoked ☐ cigarettes	430-431

WEDNESDAY

For each part of the day: **1** Answer the question about what you did by ticking **Yes** or **No**.   and   **2** **If you did not smoke** during that part of the day write 0 in the box.

If you smoked during that part of the day write in the box the number of cigarettes you smoked yourself.

		Tick one box		Number of cigarettes smoked		
		Yes / No				
Early morning	Did you get up and go to school?	☐ ☐	→	I smoked ☐ cigarettes		432-433
Morning	Were you at school all morning?	☐ ☐	→	I smoked ☐ cigarettes		434-435
Dinner Time	Did you stay on the school premises all dinnertime?	☐ ☐	→	I smoked ☐ cigarettes		436-437
Afternoon	Were you at school all afternoon?	☐ ☐	→	I smoked ☐ cigarettes		438-439
Tea Time	Did you have your tea at home?	☐ ☐	→	I smoked ☐ cigarettes		440-441
Evening	Did you stay at home all evening?	☐ ☐	→	I smoked ☐ cigarettes		442-443

THURSDAY

For each part of the day: **1** Answer the question about what you did by ticking **Yes** or **No**.   and   **2** **If you did not smoke** during that part of the day write 0 in the box.

If you smoked during that part of the day write in the box the number of cigarettes you smoked yourself.

		Tick one box		Number of cigarettes smoked		
		Yes / No				
Early morning	Did you get up and go to school?	☐ ☐	→	I smoked ☐ cigarettes		444-445
Morning	Were you at school all morning?	☐ ☐	→	I smoked ☐ cigarettes		446-447
Dinner Time	Did you stay on the school premises all dinnertime?	☐ ☐	→	I smoked ☐ cigarettes		448-449
Afternoon	Were you at school all afternoon?	☐ ☐	→	I smoked ☐ cigarettes		450-451
Tea Time	Did you have your tea at home?	☐ ☐	→	I smoked ☐ cigarettes		452-453
Evening	Did you stay at home all evening?	☐ ☐	→	I smoked ☐ cigarettes		454-455

FRIDAY

For each part of the day: **1** Answer the question about what you did by ticking **Yes** or **No**.   and **2** **If you did not smoke** during that part of the day write 0 in the box.

If you smoked during that part of the day write in the box the number of cigarettes you smoked yourself.

		Tick one box		Number of cigarettes smoked	
		Yes	No		
Early morning	Did you get up and go to school?	☐ 1	☐ 2	→ I smoked ☐ cigarettes	456-457
Morning	Were you at school all morning?	☐ 1	☐ 2	→ I smoked ☐ cigarettes	458-459
Dinner Time	Did you stay on the school premises all dinnertime?	☐ 1	☐ 2	→ I smoked ☐ cigarettes	460-461
Afternoon	Were you at school all afternoon?	☐ 1	☐ 2	→ I smoked ☐ cigarettes	462-463
Tea Time	Did you have your tea at home?	☐ 1	☐ 2	→ I smoked ☐ cigarettes	464-465
Evening	Did you stay at home all evening?	☐ 1	☐ 2	→ I smoked ☐ cigarettes	466-467

SATURDAY

For each part of the day: **1** Answer the question about what you did by ticking **Yes** or **No**.   and **2** **If you did not smoke** during that part of the day write 0 in the box.

If you smoked during that part of the day write in the box the number of cigarettes you smoked yourself.

		Tick one box		Number of cigarettes smoked	
		Yes	No		
Early morning	Did you get up later than you do on weekdays?	☐ 1	☐ 2	→ I smoked ☐ cigarettes	468-469
Morning	Were you at home all morning?	☐ 1	☐ 2	→ I smoked ☐ cigarettes	470-471
Dinner Time	Did you have your dinner or snack at home?	☐ 1	☐ 2	→ I smoked ☐ cigarettes	472-473
Afternoon	Were you at home all afternoon?	☐ 1	☐ 2	→ I smoked ☐ cigarettes	474-475
Tea Time	Did you have your tea or evening meal at home?	☐ 1	☐ 2	→ I smoked ☐ cigarettes	476-477
Evening	Did you stay at home all evening?	☐ 1	☐ 2	→ I smoked ☐ cigarettes	478-479

Spare 480

SUNDAY

For each part of the day:

1 Answer the question about what you did by ticking **Yes** or **No**.

and **2** **If you did not smoke** during that part of the day write 0 in the box.

If you smoked during that part of the day write in the box the number of cigarettes you smoked yourself.

		Tick one box			Number of cigarettes smoked		
		Yes	No				
Early morning	Did you get up later than you do on weekdays?	☐ 1	☐ 2	→	I smoked	☐ cigarettes	508-509
Morning	Were you at home all morning?	☐ 1	☐ 2	→	I smoked	☐ cigarettes	510-511
Dinner Time	Did you have your dinner or snack at home?	☐ 1	☐ 2	→	I smoked	☐ cigarettes	512-513
Afternoon	Were you at home all afternoon?	☐ 1	☐ 2	→	I smoked	☐ cigarettes	514-515
Tea Time	Did you have your tea or evening meal at home?	☐ 1	☐ 2	→	I smoked	☐ cigarettes	516-517
Evening	Did you stay at home all evening?	☐ 1	☐ 2	→	I smoked	☐ cigarettes	518-519

This book is ... for ...